Look Up

My Battle with Leukemia and What I Have Learned

Larry M Mazzotti

ISBN-13: 9781735626710

Library of Congress Control Number: 2020915774
Printed in the United States of America

Dedication

To my beautiful bride because without her, none of this could have been done. And to everyone going through a serious health crisis and their care givers.

Table of Contents

Preface

When the doctor tells you, "You've got cancer.", your whole life stops and everything going forward changes. You must quickly educate yourself on medical terms and technologies that apply to your specific diagnosis. Decisions must be made immediately on how to treat your condition and then how to manage all other aspects of your life as the treatments proceed.

The impact goes way beyond just you. Your family, friends, co-workers, and anyone else that knows you are affected by your situation. It affects your close and casual relationships, your work and how each days' tasks are managed and accomplished. Normal planned schedules are replaced by "it depends on how I am doing at the moment" living.

My wife experienced this at age 40 in 1998 with breast cancer, and then I was diagnosed with leukemia at age 49 in 2009.

After being her caregiver and then becoming the patient myself, I found the challenges in both roles are huge and at times extremely difficult to manage. Watching your loved one go through horrible pain and not being able to help her is very frustrating and agonizing. The caregiver also must manage everything else going on with the family and work. Along with that, there are constant communications with everyone around asking how the patient is doing and their status. I found that managing all these things while trying to encourage my wife and keep my own attitude positive is like trying to swim upstream in the Mississippi River.

However, when I became the patient and was going through my own medical treatments with all their side effects (physical, mental, emotional, and spiritual), I gained much more empathy for anyone going through serious health situations. The regular checkups that used to be no big deal are now very daunting. Will my body have another problem? What will these test results show? Now I am the one on the exam table getting poked and prodded, and I see my wife with a look of painful worry about me. As I went through my own cancer battle and she took over the caregiver role, we were able to help each other cope since we both had been on the other side.

Over the last few years as I shared our experiences with friends and family, several people encouraged me to write a book about what we went through and how we were able to get through these difficult years. So, in July 2017, I began to review old calendars and information from our past and started writing what we went through chronologically. Fortunately, my wife has a college degree in communications and her writing skills were critical in taking what I had written and provide the prose for the book.

After three years and many edits and revisions, we accomplished our goal. We hope that what you read in the upcoming chapters will be an inspiration and provide you some new perspectives and knowledge on how to navigate through your own or someone else's major health challenge.

Chapter 1

History and Diagnosis

In 2009, typical for lazy, late June days in Illinois, it was warm. My golfing days were few and far between because I was usually too busy to golf, but it seemed like a nice day to go out and just hit a few around the course. I never used a cart because I knew walking was best for me. At 49 years old, I believed I was in the best health condition of my life. Little did I know my world would soon turn upside down.

I live in the Midwest, near Decatur, Illinois, the heart of our state's agricultural community. Joyce and I were married in 1989, and within two months I attained custody of my then five-year-old daughter, Amy, and 20-month-old daughter, Jodi. Joyce had a five-year-old son, Justin, from her prior marriage, and the challenges of managing a five-person blended family household began in earnest. In addition, there were job changes, the death of both of our dads, and Joyce's health issues, all major life stressors consuming time and energy those first 20 years of our marriage.

In 1997, just after turning 40, Joyce found a lump in in her left breast. The biopsy revealed it was cancer, and she would need to undergo treatment. She had both a lumpectomy and mastectomy in January 1998, followed by four rounds of chemotherapy.

During this time, we still had three children at home, and I found being a caregiver was a much more difficult role than I thought it would be. As her husband, watching her suffer through chemo treatments and surgeries while knowing I could do nothing to alleviate any of it, these days were emotionally painful and stressful for me. In addition, the chemo caused her to go through an immediate *chemical menopause*. With a wife in menopause as well as kids going through puberty, the climate in our home was sometimes hurricane-like.

While the treatment was successful in eliminating the cancer, Joyce continued to get cysts in the other breast. Although none of these cysts was cancer, each set in motion a horrible roller coaster of emotions that neither she nor I wanted to keep enduring. Consequently, she decided to have the other breast removed in 2006.

In 2006 Jodi moved out, and Justin graduated from college in 2007. Officially *empty nesters*, we were ready to enjoy the leisure time and traveling we had not been able to do. My mother was still alive and lived about an hour from us, and in 2002 we had moved my mother-in-law to a home about five blocks from our house. I was self- employed as a computer consultant, and Joyce did custom logo and embroidery from our home. Being self-employed had it perks, but I never took for granted that health was an enduring blessing. I knew my body needed its tune-ups just as my car did.

Since the age of 40 (and especially after Joyce's diagnosis at 40), I was diligent about getting annual blood tests for all the standard parameters, and the outcomes were always well within normal ranges. I had a real phobia of needles, and hearing the doctor say I would only need to do this once a year was more than fine with me. Throughout my entire life, I was blessed to have never been diagnosed with any serious health issue. With none of the previous blood tests showing any problems and after having a complete physical in May of 2009, I had gotten the all clear. At 49 years of life, I was good to go, and life was wonderful. I valued my physical health and had been very health conscious since 1984.

Back then, my weight increased to over 200 pounds on my 5' 10" frame. At age 24, I realized that I had to change my approach to what I ate and my activity level. This weight increase occurred after I graduated from college in 1982 and secured an engineering position with IBM. A couple of years in this professional occupation gave me a lot of meetings and desk time. As many people do, I continued to eat and drink at the level of my teenage and college years but with much less physical activity; it was taking its toll.

One day in 1984, I stepped on a balance beam scale that had the two horizontal sliders and placed the bottom one on

150. I pushed it further, further, continuing to slide the top one to the right, but it went all the way and never moved. That had never happened to me before, which meant only one thing—I weighed over 200 pounds!

I can still picture moving that bottom slider to the 200 position and top slider to two. I then took a good look in the mirror at myself and did not like what I saw. Some fat guy who had a couple of chins, man-boobs, and a pretty pronounced spare tire around his waist was staring back at me. I could not even walk for nine holes of golf back then without becoming out of breath. Seeing others struggling with this and watching them on the roller coaster short-term diets, I decided that I needed to begin a sustainable healthier lifestyle to bring my weight down and improve my overall fitness. These lifestyle changes included the following:

Increasing physical activity, which ultimately lead me to become an aerobics instructor for 10 years.

Reducing amount of food consumed (Eat to Live, not Live to Eat).

Substituting unhealthy food and drink choices with healthy ones (Goodbye beer, regular soda, hamburgers, French fries, fried chicken, etc.).

Drinking water and chewing sugar-free gum when hungry for snacks.

Supplementing my diet with vitamins and natural products to strengthen my immune system.

From my peak at 202 pounds in 1984, I was down to 150 by 1989 and able to run over a mile without extreme effort. Even that horrible slice in my golf swing got corrected by being more flexible and having a higher level of cardio endurance. However, with this increased physical activity, I realized that I felt and looked better at around 160; therefore, I maintained my weight between 155 and 165 from that point. I really focused on how my clothing fit and how I felt instead of the actual weight. This kept me from monitoring the scale too much and kept my perspective on my real goal: managing my physical body to maximize my energy levels, flexibility, strength, mental sharpness, and emotional health.

After achieving and maintaining this level of fitness, I advised others, through aerobics classes I taught and social circles, what had worked for me to sustain this. I did not slide back into the old habits. An added benefit was not getting sick as often as before from the typical colds and flu that came with raising three children. I stopped the aerobics instructing in the early 2000s, but continued to exercise regularly and with the healthy lifestyle, maintained this fitness level through my 40's.

The other major change in my life that occurred in 1984, besides deciding to live healthier, was coming to know the Lord. After achieving my education and career goals, I found that at age 24 I had realized everything I had worked towards during my early years. I had a great job and work environment, a family, new car, house, friends and plenty of fun, extracurricular activities.

However, this was not bringing me the satisfaction that I thought it would. I was involved in a bowling league and my friend there, who also was an IBM engineer, told me about his faith in Jesus Christ and how studying the Bible provided him answers and direction in life that I was wondering about myself. I had grown up in a mainline church and never really pursued more in-depth knowledge. He told me to purchase a NIV Study Bible and read the New Testament on my own to come to my own conclusions. After I read the New Testament, I joined his church and small group study on Thursday nights, experienced the life changing impact of receiving Jesus Christ as my personal Lord and Savior, and began an ongoing study of the Bible and a relationship with Jesus. Now I had His guidance and direction in my life and no longer had to just rely on my own experience and intellect. Life was good in so many ways, I could not imagine then the turn it was about to take.

As I was inching towards this milestone mark of 50, I did have days when I would tire more easily. Not anxiety-inducing, it was nothing that a Sunday afternoon nap would not cure, but it did seem to occur more often. I just attributed it to the normal aging process and being close to 50.

The other odd thing I experienced was sometimes my body would get so warm at night that I was really putting off heat—much like a person does when they have a fever. My wife Joyce would comment how warm my skin felt; but because I did not feel ill, I never actually took my temperature. I had no night sweats, so I just attributed all of this again to the normal aging process. I felt that my routine of exercise was critical at this time; so, when those golf clubs beckoned me on that day in late June, I decided to hit the links.

Unexpectedly, while I was standing there on the course, a large strange-looking bug bit me on the leg. It did not hurt particularly badly, but within a day or so, I had nearly an inch diameter reddened area on my leg. I also noticed that my lymph glands around my neck, under my arms, and at the top of my legs were swollen. Not painful or large, they were just about the size of cranberries. The bite looked so odd, and these symptoms were so unusual, that I decided not to take any chances and get this checked by our family doctor. When I saw him on June 29, 2009, he told me that this was probably a viral infection like mononucleosis, not the bug bite, that my body's immune system was fighting. He had me get a blood test the next day to see exactly what was going on. With all of this, I was not in any way thinking that the swollen lymph glands indicated anything serious.

A few days later, the blood test results came in, and he called me and told me that he was referring me to the local oncology medical group. I was stunned and asked what he thought I had going on. He would not tell me anything because he was not sure. Since my white blood count was elevated, he wanted the cancer care group (who are also hematologists) to perform additional tests; because if he ordered these tests and then sent me there, they would repeat the same tests. My family doctor did not want me to have to go through these tests twice since he knew about my *needle-phobia*.

Because of the 4th of July holiday, I could not get in to

get the results right away. Those few days seemed like an eternity. In the middle of the afternoon on a hot July 8, 2009, while we were sitting in a local oncologist's exam room, I had an unpleasant flashback. This waiting experience brought back memories for both me and my wife.

Back in 1997 at the age of 40, she was diagnosed with breast cancer and this very same doctor was her oncologist. Fortunately for my wife, she successfully battled her breast cancer, and after ten years the doctor did not feel she needed more follow up. I thought we were finished seeing the inside of this place. Trust me when I say this is NOT the type of place where you want to be on the family plan. Anxieties were running high.

The familiar scene dredged up a memory of one of her chemotherapy treatments when I glanced and saw them trying to get the needle in her arm. I started feeling dizzy, sick to my stomach, and was told I was turning shades of green. One of the nurses looked at me and shouted, "Sit down and put your head between your legs!" I almost passed out and it took me a while to get over feeling nauseous.

In my wife's subsequent treatments, the cancer center nurses would laugh and say that when my wife came in for a treatment, two beds were needed--one for her and one for me! It was good to find some humor in this place, and what really amazed me was that these caring nurses were surprised that a husband was bringing his wife to her treatments. They told us that this was very unusual. Most of the time, the patient's female relative or friend would bring her. In fact, many women receiving cancer treatments got no support from their husbands and even experience the men leaving their marriages. I was amazed that we men could be so shallow and self-centered.

I had the best doctor though, and I knew it. Dr. James Wade is outstanding in his field and a pillar of our medical community. He was always incredibly supportive of my wife's activities, provided impeccable care for her, and was instrumental in her regaining her health. To provide recognition for the milestones of each survivor and their practices, the two hospitals in town hold an annual survivor event. One year they asked me to get on stage to dance with the doctors. They played the Chicken Dance and YMCA songs with a crazy guy leading them, and for some reason I got volunteered. Apparently, I did such a good job (remember I had taught aerobics for 10 years) that he made sure to have me called up every year. Probably no one else wanted the job, but as the event grew year after year I became "Doctor Mazzotti" as an inside joke. Multiple times, I had people ask me when I had joined their practice. Eventually the dancing became an annual part in the program. Through all of this, we developed a great relationship with this oncologist and the people in their practice, so coming to him was very comforting to us. I even would call him "Coach" since he called "the plays."

But today was no fun, sunny afternoon leading a dance. Here we were again, in the office, and I was hoping this would not be "my turn" as an oncology patient. I glanced at the wall at the colorful paintings we had seen too many times and then in the chair by the door at my wife who was looking down at the cold tile floor. All I could think of is "how strange?" For years, she was on the exam table and I was in the chair. All those memories, when I had been the caregiver and she had been the patient, from her cancer battle came flooding back to me. Now would the roles be exchanged?

Dr. Wade always whistles before he comes in the room. You know he is about to enter when you hear the Sinatra strains getting louder as he comes down the hallway. When he walked in, we both took a deep breath while he explained the diagnosis which was determined by my blood work. I had a white blood count of 80,000 (normal range is 3,000 – 11,000) and from what they could assess, I had CLL (Chronic Lymphocytic Leukemia). He said that since it was chronic, he recommended monitoring my blood counts every three months to see if it progressed to a point where treatment would be needed. We found out that about a third of people diagnosed with CLL would never need treatments because the disease does not get to a dangerous level, and many don't even need their first treatment until 5-10 years after they are diagnosed. CLL is somewhat of a crock-pot or slow growing type of cancer. Even if it did get to a level that required treatment, there were effective chemotherapy medicines that would keep it in remission. He examined me thoroughly and checked my spleen as well.

He told us that in this type of cancer, the body creates too many white blood cells that have no purpose. He called them *puts* cells. He said they just accumulate and take up space that the healthy cells should have. They also take up space in the blood stream and crowd out the function of the healthy red, white and platelet cells. Eventually, they accumulate in the lymph glands and spleen, which is why I was having enlarged lymph nodes all over my body. He could not really ascertain why my doctor did not notice them during my physical exam just two months prior to that, nor why I had not felt them until just recently. I really had no idea how long I had this cancer in my body, but it was now making its ugly presence known.

He gave us a book to give us further information about the disease, and I learned that only one percent of the people to get CLL get diagnosed before the age of 50. I was in that one percent, and although his initial assessment was very encouraging, that one percent number made me slowly start to feel like my run of good health was starting to run out. The next step to be done that day was a bone marrow biopsy which would be needed to determine more about the specifics of the type of CLL I had.

They led me into another room and had me lie face down while a local anesthetic was injected into my hip area. The doctor took a tool which could only be described as a corkscrew-like device and slowly began twisting it into my skin and my hip bone beneath it. For someone who cringed at the sight of a blood draw, this experience was beyond belief and seemed to last an eternity. The doctor joked that I must drink a lot of milk, because my bones were rock hard. Gee, thanks doc—could you move it along a bit? For a guy who had a phobia for needles, getting my hip drilled and bone marrow aspirated was a real shock. This biopsy made me realize that a needle drawing blood was no big deal and got me over this fear very quickly, which was a good thing.

When the tool was finally removed, a compression bandage was placed on my hip, and I had to stay immobile for several minutes while the bleeding subsided. My sample would be sent away for further testing and in a few weeks, we would know a little more about this beast I would be fighting. Joyce was not in the room, and I could only imagine how she felt, knowing I was going through this grueling test. Later when she came into the room, and the doctor left to make my next appointment, I saw the tears streaming down my wife's face and remembered how hard it was for me to be her caregiver. Now with our roles reversed, we both would begin to experience the other's perspective, and we would have to bring back out our "Survival Kit" again. Please see Appendix 1 for what this kit contained.

Look Up

Chapter 2

Monitoring and Initial Treatment (Jul 2009 – Jan 2011)

Since I had never *felt sick* from the CLL, I was really struggling with believing this was truly happening. I had only mild fatigue and very few symptoms, other than the swollen lymph glands. I think now that these were early signs of the leukemia starting to grow in my body, and the swollen lymph glands were just the next step in the progression. We continued our daily life routines while wondering if this leukemia was going to become a bigger issue.

These routines in 2009 included my wife and I running our own home-based businesses and my piano playing in various community settings, as well as watching our two-year old granddaughter several days and evenings a week. I began eleven years of private lessons in 1967 at age seven and always found much satisfaction and enjoyment in piano. Since I was never a good athlete when I was in school, music was my chosen activity for elective classes and engagements outside of school.

During my school years, I played piano, guitar, and alto saxophone in various music groups, including school bands, rock bands, jazz combos and solo piano gigs at several restaurants and night clubs in the Springfield, Illinois area. Since my piano teacher was playing at many locales, he gave me extra copies of his music. As I started my career years, I continued to play solo in restaurants, senior living centers, weddings, and other special events. With the copies of my teacher's music and more that I had purchased, I developed many songs in my repertoire. Playing music has always been very emotionally therapeutic for me and using this talent that God has given me provides a deep inner contentment that is hard to describe. This feeling is especially strong when playing music in senior centers and at church services where helping people worship the Lord is always an uplifting experience. This *music therapy* would be a key benefit to me later in the cancer battle.

After I graduated from University of Illinois with a Bachelor of Science in Ceramic Engineering in June 1982, I worked for IBM in Endicott, New York, as an engineer in product engineering until 1986, then moved back to Central Illinois to become an IBM marketing representative for local manufacturing companies. This job lasted until 40% of us got *surplused* in March 1993. My wife was an Allstate Insurance claims adjuster who quit her job in June 1993 to stay home and be a full-time mom for our three children. Since family obligations prevented us from moving out of state for me to pursue another engineering job, I worked for local computer dealers and built up a good number of small business clients over the next 12 years. When the last company I was working for got out of the computer business in 2005, I continued to service my computer customers providing sales, service, and consulting to them and would go to their facilities frequently to install new systems and fix problems. However, this did not entail overnight trips since all my computer customers were located within one hour of my home office. This allowed me to be there for my family every night.

Running our own businesses provided flexibility in scheduling as this cancer battle became more intense. We continued to work and live pretty much normally through the rest of 2009 and into 2010. By October 16, 2009, the white blood count was up to about 120,000 and by January 28, 2010, it was up to 180,000. That month Joyce and I drove to West Virginia in the Appalachian Mountains. We rented snowshoes and hiked trails leading up the side of one of these mountains. I was still not experiencing any major fatigue and felt assured that the disease was still progressing slowly.

Our cancer care center had recently opened a new facility, and we were asked by Dr. Wade to participate in a television commercial for it. He told us that we would be on camera with other survivors and maybe interviewed as a group. Well, we showed up on February 1, 2010 in the late afternoon for the filming of this and found out we were it! Dr. Wade was there, and the video crew shot several scenes of us with him. In one scene, I was pretending receiving a chemotherapy treatment, and I thought, boy am I glad I got CLL and will probably never need to do this for real. (Ha!)

The commercial aired during the 2010 Winter Olympics on our local television station, and unexpectedly many people told us that we were an inspiration to them! Little did we know that this was just the beginning of a long journey, and the fake chemotherapy treatment would soon be replaced with the real thing.

Unfortunately, by May 2010, my white count was over 230,000. This rapid progression meant it was time for another bone marrow biopsy which revealed that 70% of my marrow was leukemia cells and only 30% was creating healthy cells. I also kept track of my lymph nodes, which were increasing in size along with swelling around my ankles. The upwards trend was there, and Dr. Wade did not want to wait any longer to start treatment. My bone marrow biopsy also revealed my brand of CLL was something called *unmutated* with some chromosomal deletions. At the time all this really meant little to us, but we sensed the luxury of getting to watch and wait a long time before starting treatment was gone. The next phase of this journey was about to unfold.

Up to this point, I only saw the cancer as some numbers on blood tests, and I thoroughly hated getting stuck with needles to get those tests. Since I had no significant negative symptoms, this disease was not *real* to me, and I was even questioning the necessity and veracity of these blood tests. Since I trusted my oncologist, I agreed to proceed with my first rounds of chemotherapy.

Each round of chemotherapy was going to take five days

with three weeks break in between each round. I had signed up to participate in a study, which meant the protocol was set to give me up to six rounds of chemotherapy followed with an oral medication for six months. With that many rounds of chemo and each round taking five days, the doctor told me to get a port in my body a couple of weeks prior to receiving the first round of chemo medications and blood draws. I had no idea what that meant.

I discovered I had to get something called a *Power Port* installed in me to receive chemotherapy treatments. On June 4, 2010, I found myself in the outpatient area of a local hospital and I was nervous. No, it was more than nervous; I was really in an indescribable emotional state.

A nurse came in and showed us what the *Power Port* looked like and explained how the procedure would be done. This caused me even more anxiety because I was imagining a rather small device like an IV needle. In reality this was about the size of a soda bottle cap that would be completely under the skin on my chest with a tube, also under my skin, connecting the *Power Port* to my jugular vein at the base of my neck.

"Really? Are you kidding me?? Come on now, there must be some mistake! All that hardware is going to be put INSIDE my body? What if the doctor slips with the scalpel and severs my jugular vein? What if I get an infection? Isn't there some other option here?" All kinds of crazy thoughts were running through my mind, and I felt like this was a horrible nightmare! "Come on, Larry; wake up!!"

I found out reality sometimes has a very abrupt way of communicating and unfortunately, I was not responding back. I completely shut down. As the nurse asked me simple yes-and-no questions, I could only nod or shake my head which was already looking down at the floor. I was so void of any intelligent response that it got to the point where my wife said, "Answer the lady, Hon." The nurse asked me if I needed to use the restroom, and I was unable to acknowledge even verbally that. She left the room while I changed into my gown and proceeded down the hallway to the restroom for yet another of my *nervous pees* that morning.

When I returned, the nurse came in, walked me to the operating room, and had me lay down on the table. I felt like I was being led to the executioner. I still did not utter a single word. Staring at the ceiling and looking at the equipment all around me, I went back to the idea that this was a bad nightmare that I just needed to awaken from to stop!

As the team continued to prepare me, I felt like jumping off the table and running out of there. Maybe God would just swoop in and rescue me now? I tried to mentally reason with myself to calm down and relax but my frightened, stupid self would have none of that. Nurses then came in, packed me with blankets and started the sleepy medicine. I felt utterly helpless and totally out of control. When the doctor came in, I was only half cognizant but could feel him inject the local pain medicine into my right chest and neck areas. I slipped in and out of consciousness and remember tugs on the skin as he put the Power Port hardware in my upper right chest area and connected the tube into the jugular vein at the base of my neck on the right side.

After the doctor finished, I was assisted onto a gurney and wheeled into the recovery room. I lay there with my upper body canted at about a 45-degree angle. In shock and not able to comprehend what just happened, I stared out into space and still could not even bring myself to talk. My wife tried to communicate, but I just shook my head in answer to her questions. The nurse came in to check on me and told me that I needed to drink something, but I just reacted by shaking my head side to side that I did not want anything. Joyce got irritated at my lack of response and told me to please talk to the nurse. I then managed to tell the nurse to get me something to drink and eat so I could get out of here. The anxiety began to wane, and with substantial bandages on my right chest and lower right part of my neck, I got dressed and was wheeled out to our car.

As my wife drove us home, we discussed my inability to communicate and my reactions before and after the procedure. This was the first medical surgery I ever had where my chest and neck were cut open and obviously, I could not begin to process this mentally or emotionally. We got home and I continued to struggle with what had just happened. I just never envisioned this process heading in this direction. Little did I know I was only on the very tip of the treatment iceberg.

That night when I tried to lay down in bed, the muscles

in my neck and upper chest areas began to spasm. Not small spasms that are barely detectable, but full-blown spasms that looked like an alien inside struggling to escape my body. My jugular vein was galloping like an electric wire on a windy day, and I could not stop shaking and chilling from the muscle spasms. This was a horrible sensation because I thought it would dislodge the internal hardware or cause an internal bleed. My wife immediately called the after-hours number we had been given, and I was told to just try to relax. I put on more clothing for warmth and sat up to get the spasms to subside. I realized now I could not just lay down like I always had done. After I got warmer and stopped shaking, the muscle spasms abated. I now very carefully laid down in bed on my left side to try and get some sleep. Although I was able to recline without experiencing muscle contractions in my neck and chest, sleep was not easily obtained. I did eventually fall asleep but had a restless night.

The next step was a CT scan with contrast on June 14. This is where I discovered that I am allergic to the iodine that is injected for the CT scan contrast. After they put the iodine in me through the Power Port that was now in my right chest, I lit up like a red lightbulb and my skin itched. The rash came on quickly and seemed to bloom even more as the day went on. Eventually this subsided and from then on, I had to take Benadryl and steroids prior to getting any CT scan with contrast.

The scan detected two nickel-sized spots on my liver. More anxiety came as I thought the cancer had gotten in my liver. Dr. Wade reviewed the scans and told me they were *hemangiomas*—clusters of blood vessels that had probably been there since birth.

I also learned that not only does the needle hurt when put in the Power Port, but it also hurts when removed. Although the nurse does not have to try to hit a vein, I still feel the needle punch through my skin and when it is removed every time. Somewhere in my mind I remembered when my two daughters were born how the medical people recommended Lamaze breathing during painful episodes. I employed this when I needed to, and it did help some. I just had to learn to endure the physical pain.

On June 17, I received another bone marrow biopsy at the local cancer care center to get a view of the leukemia in my marrow for the study that I was participating in. I took some meds to help me relax, but these did nothing for me to decrease the pain. The local anesthetic was injected in my hip, and Dr. Wade drilled into my bone on the opposite side from the last time.

Joyce got to observe Dr. Wade performing this procedure. This time the pain was so intense that I came up off the table when he aspirated to get the bone marrow sample. The compression bandage was applied, and I turned over to wait for the nurse to check me for bleeding. I was beginning to feel like a pin cushion and a piece of machined metal that kept being drilled. As I sat there in pain with some tears and frustration, I saw my wife's expression of worry and sadness. A feeling of guilt came over me, knowing I was the cause of her being sad. I always wanted to make my wife feel good and happy, and after 20+ years of marriage, I felt like I had done that well. But now, causing her this kind of grief was especially hard for me to accept. In some ways, that hurt worse than getting drilled.

Recovery from these latest three procedures (Power Port, CT Scan, and Bone Marrow Biopsy) was another new experience for me. I could not just leave after them to go back to work or some other activity. The residual pain and other issues caused me to have to stay home for longer times than ever before. Struggling to deal with this, I had no idea how isolation would present a much bigger challenge.

On Monday June 21, Joyce and I came to the local cancer care center as soon as they opened to get my first round of chemo. Another couple we knew were also in infusion that day with the husband getting a treatment. Being there all day, it was nice to have someone to talk to for part of the time. The nurse that took care of me was the same one who gave chemo to Joyce when she battled breast cancer. Amazing how these connections occurred to give us some level of comfort.

She accessed my Power Port (ouch again), drew blood, and started my pre-meds. I discovered another unique characteristic of my body. I do not need the *normal* dosage of medicines for effectiveness—I need less. After getting the *normal* 50 mg dose of Benadryl, my legs started shaking uncontrollably. I learned another new word, *rigors*, which is apparently what these shakes are called. Another med was given to me to counteract it, and after my body settled down, the nurse started the chemo. The infusion rate of the first chemo drug, Rituximab, was initiated at a slow pace, but even at that, my body started to react. The chemo had to be stopped for a brief period, then resumed once my body calmed down. Nine hours after we arrived, we left the first chemo session.

Since I was part of a study, the protocol of chemo drugs for Round 1 was Rituximab and Fludarabine on Monday, Wednesday, Friday and just Fludarabine on Tuesday and Thursday. With getting the pre-meds and both chemo drugs, we were the first ones there and the last ones to leave on Monday, Wednesday, and Friday of that week.

After Monday's session, my legs and ankles swelled due to the leukemia cells being killed off and my kidneys not being able to keep up. This became extremely painful and my skin was stretched to the point where I thought it might split open. I got meds to reduce this, but that took several days. Looking like the Michelin Man, I struggled painfully to walk or even sit.

Even with all the adjustments to counter side effects we successfully completed the first round of chemo on June 25. With the slower rates, I did not get terribly sick, but I did have some negative effects including feeling queasy and very fatigued after each day. On Tuesdays and Thursdays, I was able to do computer work since the chemo treatments were only a couple of hours. I was determined to try to continue working and doing my normal activities as much as possible during these chemo treatments.

I came back to cancer care and got a blood draw on June 29 and met with Dr. Wade on June 30 for a follow-up appointment. The unexpected issues in the first round prompted Dr. Wade to adjust the pre-meds and to provide other meds for my reactions. Fortunately, these issues were not severe enough to put me completely down. I continued working on computers, helping Joyce with the garment business, and playing piano.

July 16 was our American Cancer Society Relay for Life event at the local community college and unlike last year, I now had begun to experience the actual treatments and tests. This gave me much more empathy for other survivors. Because Joyce and I had done television commercials for our new cancer care center, we got to interact with many people. This is also when I began to understand that being a Christian does not provide some formula or special dispensation for avoiding suffering. We all experience it in various settings and forms; however, Jesus promised to never leave us or forsake us.(Hebrews 13:5) Psalm 23 states: *"Even though I walk through the darkest valley, I will fear no evil, for you are with me."* As we were talking and encouraging many people, I saw some deeper purposes for this cancer battle. Would I allow this situation to take away my joy and positive attitude? As we survivors shared our experiences, I became more aware that this situation was not just about me and my health condition. Could it be that it was more about how I handled the pain and uncertainty with a positive confidence in my Creator? Is trusting in Him and not my own strength a key ingredient for not only my survival but for being able to help others through their cancer battles, too? It was apparent God was changing me and my perspectives.

Round two of my chemotherapy started first thing on Monday, July 19, at our local cancer care center. This time we got a private room to provide me more rest time and less interaction with people in the main infusion area. Because I knew this would be a long process again, I wanted to be able to rest as much as possible.

The initial blood test, however, revealed my good white blood cell count was too low to receive the Fludarabine chemo med. Rituximab only was given slowly after the pre-meds and we left around 1:00pm. After taking a nap at home that afternoon, I resumed my computer work later that day and the next day. On Wednesday, July 21, I got my blood checked and the good white cell count was high enough to receive the Fludarabine chemo med. However, since I had to get five consecutive days of Fludarabine per the study that I was participating in, I received this through my Power Port on Wednesday, Thursday, and Friday, then took Fludarabine chemo pills on Saturday and Sunday (4 pills each day) along with a Kytril anti-nausea pill. I was instructed to use gloves and not allow anyone else to handle these chemo pills. Lots of precautions for something that I was swallowing certainly made me wonder about the strong medicine that was contained in them.

One Thursday before I went in for chemo, I took my granddaughter for a walk and she reached out and touched a poison oak plant. We got back home, and I washed both of us very thoroughly. I ended up getting a rash anyway and had to get topical meds for this on top of everything else I was taking. I was concerned this would negatively impact my cancer treatment since my immune system was compromised, but fortunately the topical med worked on the poison oak rash with no negative impact to my chemo treatments. This again caused anxiety about possible problems this could cause during my treatments and more frustration about why this happened now.

On July 29, Joyce and I were at the local State of Illinois women's prison to be the main speakers at their Relay for Life event. I had been playing piano for the Release Through Jesus Prison Ministry group from 2002 through 2008 and had spent many Sundays at the prison playing and taught a *Purpose Driven Life* class on Tuesday afternoons over a three-month period. Therefore, I had gotten to know some inmates and they knew me. Joyce had also spoken there on several occasions for breast cancer awareness. This provided a great connection with the inmates for both of us to be speakers for their Relay for Life event and again reinforced the importance of focusing on helping others more than thinking about my personal struggles. Would these inmates see a different Larry now than the person they saw before? I guess it is one thing to teach about a purpose driven life, but it is another to live it out during difficult circumstances.

I remembered from Joyce's four rounds of chemotherapy for her breast cancer battle that after each additional round, the impact and recovery were more difficult. This was also the case with me, although somewhat differently. On August 16, my blood was checked, again showing my good white blood count was low; however, it was so low that I could not receive any chemotherapy. Although leukemia was *bad* white blood cells, the impact of the chemotherapy medications affected all white blood cells. One of the main jobs of white blood cells is infection fighting; and if mine got too low, I could get sick from some communicable disease and have a hard time fighting it off.

Obviously, working on people's computers in various small businesses exposed me to all kinds of possible infections. I had asked Dr. Wade if I needed to stop working on computers to protect my health or continue working on computers with some additional protective measures. He recommended that unless I started having fevers and other signs of my immune system not keeping up, I could continue working on computers with more protective measures like additional hand washing, avoid shaking hands and being around anyone who exhibits signs of illness, etc.

Dr. Wade scheduled me for another blood test on Friday, August 20. We got there first thing in the morning, and this time my good white blood count was high enough to receive both chemo medications. However, after checking with the people in charge of the cancer research study that I was participating in, Dr. Wade cut the amount of Rituximab and Fludarabine chemotherapy meds in half because he said that my body was responding "robustly" to the chemotherapy. I did not need as much to get the leukemia in remission and giving me more would just negatively impact my immune system. By getting half the dosages of Rituximab and Fludarabine, we left in the early afternoon, thus reducing the impact of these side-effects that came with getting chemotherapy.

Since I started round three on a Friday rather than the usual Monday, I got the chemo pills and Kytril again for Saturday and Sunday. Monday and Tuesday, I was back at the local cancer care center getting the Fludarabine chemo med through an IV in my Power Port. On Monday, I also got another CT scan with contrast to check on the two spots on my liver, which remained the same as before. This completed round three and although I was feeling tired from the treatments, I continued working and playing piano as much as I could.

In early September, while we were watching our granddaughter, my wife noticed a large bubble-like circle on the child's abdomen. It appeared almost overnight, and we were concerned it was a spider bite. My wife took her to urgent care and the doctor there took a small culture and said they would call us as soon as they knew the results. In less than two hours, we received a call that would change our daily routine. The infection was MRSA, a highly contagious infection. She was placed on strong antibiotics and her infection cleared, but the doctors warned that it was not in my best interest for us to continue babysitting her while I was in the middle of chemotherapy and perhaps even afterwards.

Because this little two-year-old girl brightened our existence every day, we were both saddened to have this joy removed. Not having her here multiple days a week seemed like the sunshine was taken from our home. We felt bad, too, for our daughter Amy, because she would have to find other childcare arrangements during the day while she worked. She was also going to beauty school at night, so several nights a week we would keep little Ariya with us. Because those that have MRSA can become carriers of the infection, we could not risk having her in our home on such a frequent basis while my immune system was compromised.

On September 17, my blood work showed low counts but still high enough to receive chemotherapy; however, Dr. Wade decided to cut my dosages of Rituximab and Fludarabine in half again. I got both meds through my Power Port after getting my pre- meds and was able to leave in the early afternoon. Going to the cancer care infusion area and having to sit for hours while receiving multiple drugs is a very boring process. I had to learn how to occupy myself during these long days being hooked up to an IV. Sometimes I slept or felt very out of it because of the medications; but when I was with it, I read and listened to Christian music and talked with my wife and the nurses. The nurses at cancer care were wonderful, and we joked around which helped me to not be so down and stressed. These health care workers take care of patients undergoing cancer treatments every day and have a unique ability to deal with these difficult situations.

We went home, and I was able to do some computer work

at my home office the rest of that day. Again, they gave me chemo pills and Kytril to take over the weekend, and I was back at cancer care center on Monday and Tuesday afternoons getting pre-meds and Fludarabine. Although this was the fourth round and I was supposed to receive six rounds of chemotherapy for the cancer research study that I was in, Dr. Wade got approval to stop me at four rounds. My white blood counts continued to drop to the point where he was concerned that I could end up in the hospital if the counts got any lower. I was relieved to avoid getting two more rounds of chemotherapy, but the oncology study that I was participating in had a Revlimid pill that was to be taken after the chemotherapy treatments. These pills would not start until January 2011 because my body needed recovery time after the months of IV chemo.

Joyce and I joined family and friends for a bus tour in southern Illinois on October 2. Nice to get away from home, I found being with this group helpful to my attitude. Keeping connected to others is extremely important for my mental and emotional health. Nonetheless, Joyce and I were still vigilant in taking precautions to avoid picking up germs.

I came back to cancer care on October 14 for blood work and saw Dr. Wade the following day for a checkup. More blood work and a check-up were done in mid- November. No serious issues were occurring, so I continued to work and play piano at church taking the precautions to avoid picking up something. Dr. Wade also wanted me to get a flu shot, so I got one on November 16. Fortunately, no problems were encountered after getting the flu shot.

We attended the Christmas celebration at cancer care on December 9 and I was able to play piano at our church for the multiple Christmas Eve services. We had a bad winter storm on Christmas Eve and since I had practice and was playing at multiple services that evening, I went alone to church in the afternoon with no issues.

By the time Joyce tried to drive to church for one of the evening Christmas Eve services, ice had accumulated on the streets making driving extremely dangerous. My poor wife ended up sliding off the road and could not get to church. With the help of good Samaritans, she was able to get the car out of a ditch and went directly back home. When I played the 10:00PM service, the roads were in good shape enabling me to return home safely. Despite the bad weather, we still had good attendance, and no one else had any accidents or problems. Being able to play with our church band again was uplifting and helped me focus on celebrating the birth of Jesus, not on my cancer battle.

Look Up

Chapter 3

Monitoring and Cancer Relapse
(Jan 2011 – Jul 2012)

After having a good 2010 holiday season with family and friends, Joyce and I took a trip to a Michigan bed and breakfast from January 6 – 10, 2011. This was a good time to get out of town and celebrate completing my four rounds of chemotherapy without any major complications or problems.

The weather was bitterly cold, and the bed and breakfast we had booked overlooked the eastern shore of Lake Michigan. We had hoped to enjoy some snow shoeing or cross-country skiing, but the actual temperatures were hovering near zero with the wind chills even lower. It just did not seem wise to try and brave the outdoors so soon after finishing the chemo. Although we could not venture out much (I did walk out on the frozen lake for just a few minutes), I was celebrating the end of the IV chemo treatments while hoping the disease would remain at bay. I wanted desperately to finally put the swollen lymph glands and fatigue behind me. Once I returned, I would begin the next leg of the journey, which was the Revlimid pills.

Taking a short get-away trip like this has been our practice since being married in 1989. With our work and family commitments, longer trips were not feasible, so each year just Joyce and I took about four short, three-to-four-day trips where we could recharge and reconnect. On this trip the weather got so bad at one point that we were actually "snowed-in" and no travel was recommended. Although the bed and breakfast didn't offer dinner, the hostess prepared us a small meal because driving was not possible. Watching a little playoff football and interacting with each other while watching the snow blow across a frozen Lake Michigan was still a fine way to get away.

Our oasis of calm was short-lived, and on January 14, 2011, it was back to cancer care and another bone marrow biopsy from Dr. Wade to determine the status of the leukemia prior to taking the Revlimid pills for six months. This was the second half of the clinical trial that I was participating in. The good news we received then was that I was officially in remission (Yea!!) and would start taking the Revlimid pills each day for three weeks then one week off. At that time, my bone marrow showed less than 10 percent leukemia cells, which was a far cry from the 70 percent leukemia that was present prior to my beginning chemo. The side effects from these pills were supposed to be minimal, and I felt like I was starting the new year in a positive way.

Since I was in the clinical trial, I did not have to purchase this medication which was over $600 per pill. I went to see

Dr. Wade at the end of each week through mid-March getting blood and urine tests to ensure this medication was not having any adverse effects on me. With no problems taking the Revlimid pills after two rounds, I went to monthly checks at cancer care center and continued to flush my power port once a month with heparin to keep it functional. Heparin is a blood thinner type medicine that prevents the port from closing when it is not used as frequently.

During the fourth round of Revlimid pills and on my April birthday weekend, Joyce and I took a train to Chicago for a getaway and saw a couple of Cubs games. I was a little nervous being in crowds and concerned about picking up some illness, but we were cautious about touching things around me and avoiding close personal contact with anyone who appeared to be ill. The cold and flu season were past, and spring seemed like a time of promise with the way everything was proceeding. This trip went off without any problems, and I was starting to feel like maybe the worst part of this cancer battle was hopefully done. I was so grateful to be able to travel and resume some semblance of normal life again.

At the end of May, I had just completed the fifth round of Revlimid pills and got a head cold. This was concerning since my immune system was still in a weakened state. Although it took slightly longer, I was able to weather the cold and get over it without any more serious issues.

After getting my monthly blood and urine samples taken at Cancer Care, Joyce and I attended the annual Cancer Care

Survivor Dinner in June with both of us now being survivors. Joyce was now a 13-year breast cancer survivor and I was a two-year survivor.

When Joyce and I first started attending this function after her cancer ordeal, there were just a few hundred people and often held on the grounds of the cancer facility or one of the local hospitals. Now the event had morphed to well over 1200 attendees and was held in the banquet hall section of a local hotel. Seeing those numbers rise year after year was encouraging, but I can honestly say this was not a club that we wanted to be in together. I wish I could have participated like prior years dancing with the doctors. But now being a survivor and looking to the future with many concerns and questions, I was out in the audience with many other survivors with similar trepidations about their futures.

Dr. Wade decided to go ahead with the last round of Revlimid starting on June 10, and I was able to continue to maintain a regular schedule of work, piano, and family time. This included playing piano at our annual women's cancer fund raiser "Come Together, Let's Walk" at Fairview Park in late June. With our past involvement in cancer awareness and education, Joyce and I spent a lot of time talking with other survivors and caregivers. To participate and be good role models for those dealing with this difficult disease was encouraging to us. Our hearts were there to help others; when we did, many of the anxieties of dealing with our own situations were deflected. Piano for me was always a positive activity, and I could see that the music I was playing was uplifting for the crowd. Once again, I was able to look out upon hundreds of cancer survivors who had faced their illness and were celebrating their outcomes or continuing their battles.

Because piano was such an integral part of my life, I continued playing several times a month at various local senior centers including nursing homes and assisted living centers. Being my own boss gave me flexibility to play during weekdays for an hour and entertain the residents with old popular music that brought back good memories. I started this practice many years prior when my grandmother was in a nursing home. Because she struggled with depression, she often was not conversive. I decided on one visit to wheel her down to the dining area and play a few songs for her on their upright piano. As I was playing, other people in wheelchairs started coming down the hallway. This gave me an idea about using my music talent to help people in these places. I had several offers to play in bands but being out late at night would have detracted from family time. I had done that in my teen years and knew what playing in bars entailed, so I decided to not play in those places.

As I played in these centers and residence homes, activity directors shared my name and soon I was up to about eight places per month. Fortunately, I was able to maintain this even as I was getting chemotherapy, but I avoided shaking hands and getting too close to people to protect me from getting sick. Giving back to those dealing with cancer at that event gave me the same type of positive feeling as playing piano at these facilities did.

I got more checkups at Cancer Care in July and August and another bone marrow biopsy on August 26, 2011. By this point, I had learned how to handle the discomfort of getting poked and drilled.

The bone marrow biopsy is truly a drill. An instrument that resembles a corkscrew-type wine bottle opener is placed on my hip while I lay face down on the table. A small amount of lidocaine is injected, but this really does nothing to deaden the deep pain that comes with the procedure because the instrument goes through the bone and into the marrow. While the procedure is not lengthy, the pain is extremely intense as the doctor screws the end of the device through my skin, muscle, and outer layer of the hip bone into the marrow. The end of the device has a small tube-like opening, and the marrow is extracted as he does a reverse corkscrew motion to remove the device and the sample. I then must lay on the table for several minutes to allow the bleeding to stop. Dr. Wade told me from the initial time that I had extremely hard bones, which made his job and my discomfort level much more difficult. He tries to alternate sides, so that the same area is not drilled consecutively.

Fortunately, the results were good, so I was still officially in remission and doing well. We decided again to take a short trip in the middle of September to a Grand Rapids, Michigan bed & breakfast for a few days. During this trip, I noticed that I was starting to feel achy. While not urgent, it was a daily feeling of an illness with a low-grade fever. I should have taken my temperature when we returned home since the issue persisted, but at the time I assumed it to be residuals from the chemo and ignored it for the most part. A mild cough presented at times, but I judged that may have been from allergies since our area was in the middle of fall harvest season.

After a couple of weeks of no real change in these symptoms, I verified that I was running a low-grade fever and got with my family doctor on October 6 to get checked out. He ordered blood test and x-rays; then on October 11, I went to see Dr. Wade, who ordered more blood tests, flushed my power port, and did a CT scan of the chest with contrast. This time, I took Benadryl and steroids to avoid the dye reaction.

Quickly, he diagnosed me with mycoplasma (walking) pneumonia. I had no idea pneumonia could creep in like this, since I felt well most days. Certainly, September was not the time of the year when pneumonia is prevalent, and I was surprised to learn this is what had been bothering me all these weeks. After taking the prescribed antibiotics, I got over this pneumonia swiftly. While glad it was not a severe form, the realization that pneumonia could develop that rapidly was another wake-up call to how fragile my immune system was.

I saw Dr. Wade in mid-November for a follow-up exam and CT Scan to make sure the pneumonia was gone. I was happy to have recovered from pneumonia without being hospitalized. With my blood counts being down from the treatments, I was susceptible to getting sick, always a major concern with cancer patients. This first time of getting sick during my treatments prompted anxieties about getting hospitalized. I remembered this from when my wife went through chemo. It is vital to be vigilant about monitoring our health condition and be ready to take immediate action when needed to avoid more serious problems.

I was able to keep working and playing piano throughout most of the last two years because I did not experience more severe side effects from the chemotherapy medications. I considered myself fortunate not to have extreme nausea, mouth sores, debilitating fatigue, and joint pain that so many patients experience. Joyce and I let people know what my situation was, so we had my name on many prayer lists. Not only the people at our church, but many others too, were lifting us up in prayer. I know this was key in my battle with cancer. It is important to share your situation with others and be open to receiving help in whatever form that is needed, especially on the mental/emotional/spiritual fronts. Because people want to be helpful, I never refused a prayer when it was offered.

With permission from my doctor, we even got to keep our now three-year old granddaughter one overnight in November. Christmas that year was wonderful, and I was feeling fantastic. Work, music, and family functions continued for me throughout December and into January 2012. My wife and I flew out to Los Angeles to see my stepson and attend an Imprinted Sportswear Show in Long Beach, CA. Our embroidery garment business, operating since 1994 from our home, motivated us to attend one of these shows about every three years to get information from our suppliers about the latest clothing and equipment and updates to technology in this industry. I truly felt like I had put cancer on the back burner and was looking forward to the trip.

We rented a lovely home on the beach near Playa Del Rey and were able to take daily walks on the beach and really relax. The seafood and healthy produce choices available in southern California in January were a far cry from what was on the store shelves here. Although it was cool and the daytime temps were only in the upper 60's, a spring-like atmosphere fueled my optimism about where I was going with the disease. My blood counts had finally rebounded to the point that airline travel was again an option. Experiencing beautiful sunsets on the beach from the patio of the home gave me a sense of tranquility and normalcy that had been missing from my life for quite some time.

I saw the doctor again in mid-February for a checkup and all was still good. By mid-May of 2012, my oasis of calm was gone; the white blood count was starting to trend up. We knew some residual leukemia cells were left when I was told I was in remission, but I had hoped the Revlimid had eliminated those. Apparently not. Huge challenges were ahead for us in the coming months. Cancer does not take a break, and neither do other life issues. Caring for my elderly mother-in-law was about to become a much bigger focus in our lives. Those few days of beach siestas seemed much longer ago than just a few months.

When my father-in-law died in 1999 from acute leukemia at age of 94, the care of my mother-in-law fell to us. She lived in Breese (southern Illinois) for about three years after he had passed, but the over-100-mile distance and the condition of her home dictated a change needed to be made. We were fortunate at the time to find her a beautiful ranch home about a half-mile from our house. Since Joyce is her only child, we both assumed caregiver roles although Pauline was very independent and had lived well on her own up to this time. Now almost 10 years later, her mother at 94 years old had her own health issues while I continued to battle mine.

Pauline would randomly pass out and fall. Nothing showed up medically to determine why she had these episodes, but they kept happening, and she was also still driving her car. We tried to help her with household chores and her medicines, but she constantly refused. On July 16, 2012, she passed out and fell by the Mount Zion Post Office. After emergency treatment, and a diagnosis of a sprained right arm and a concussion, we knew she could no longer live on her own.

We convinced her to take a tour of a nearby assisted living facility about a week later with the help of our family doctor. This was a tremendous struggle because she continued to insist that she would be fine on her own even though her arm was still in a sling. We offered to get someone to come in to help her in the home, but she would not allow anyone to do this, including us. With more help from the doctor, she finally agreed to move into a one-bedroom apartment in an assisted living facility near us by the end of July.

That very same week, I was back at cancer care center getting a CT Scan, blood work, and another bone marrow biopsy. We were both concerned about this checkup because we knew the leukemia cells were trending upwards since my last visit in May.

The uncertainty and fear were very intense and we both struggled in our own ways to try and deal with it. Having plenty of work to do, the immediate needs of trying to get Pauline moved to her new place and preparing her current home for sale served as a distraction for both of us. Until this point, I had been able to continue most of my normal life routines with minimal disruptions, but now I was afraid of what may be in my future resulting in more than the usual anxieties as I prepared for my next doctor visit.

My wife and I met with Dr. Wade on 08/01/12 to review the most recent tests, and he stated that I had officially relapsed. I had been told at the beginning of this journey that this was a "crock pot type of cancer" that perhaps would not require me to have chemo for many years, if at all. The fact that I needed chemo just a couple years after the original diagnosis was diametrically opposed to everything I had been told about my disease. Now here I was, just a few months past treatment, being told I had relapsed. It was apparent to all of us now that I did not have the traditional variety CLL, but something much more aggressive.

44

I did not know it, but the biggest battle of my life with cancer was about to unfold before me and none of the things I endured prior to this would compare to what I would soon go through on a physical, emotional, and spiritual level. I was about to walk through the "valley of the shadow" that Psalm 23 spoke about, and my life would contain upheavals I could never have imagined.

Larry Mazzotti

Chapter 4

New Treatment Options and Visits to Other Doctors (Aug 2012 – Sep 2012)

Hearing that I had relapsed was extremely upsetting to both my wife and me. Remembering again that I was first told that this was a *crock pot* type of cancer, I wondered how on earth I could have relapsed so quickly. It had been about a year since I finished the Revlimid pills and I was hopeful that those and the chemo would carry me for a much longer time. Dr. Wade said it was time for another opinion and recommended Johns Hopkins in Baltimore and Siteman Cancer Center in St. Louis. The doctors there had pioneered some new treatment options, and we had run out of them here. He scheduled the appointment for the end of August in Baltimore and early September for St. Louis.

With this new mountain of stress now weighing on both of us, Joyce and I had to continue to deal with her mother's adverse attitude about the assisted living center. Many more personal belongings needed to be brought up to her apartment and gone through. Her car, many of her home furnishings, and home had to be sold. We also had to get control of her finances and bring her bill payments up to date. Upon reviewing her checking account, we found several lapses and overdue bills which further confirmed her need for help. Other financial assets were organized and documented so these could be used for her in the future.

Right before my father-in-law died in 1999, he wanted me to promise to take care of his wife, and I gave him my solemn vow that I would do that. However, she was not so receptive to our help and guidance. A few days after the devastating news about my cancer battle and relapse, I was at her assisted living apartment explaining her assets and organizing them. She stated that she wanted to go home. I told her she was at her new home now. This was a lovely, brand new facility that had just opened three months prior and had everything she could possibly need or want; however, no amount of reasoning could convince her that this beautiful new apartment was better and safer for her than her home.

Her doctor had confirmed that she could not live on her own anymore, but she would not accept his input either. Her reply was that she did not care what her doctor said and that she wanted to get back to her house. As a last resort, I pulled my chair up closer to her and informed her what my doctor told me I had to now do. I said, "At least you're 94 years old and having to do what your doctor tells you; I am only 52 and am having to do what my doctor is telling me. Given what I might have to endure, I would rather be in your situation than in mine." After that conversation, she never again complained about her move into assisted living to Joyce or me.

August 17, 2012 was my mother-in-law's 95th birthday and we had a party at her assisted living facility. While the party was not as joy filled as ones in the past, it did seem as though she had reached acceptance of her new situation and no longer talked about wanting to leave. By this point, we had sold her car and some of the household items. Unfortunately, she had been buying a lot from QVC while in her house and many of the rooms were filled from floor to ceiling with unopened boxes and brand-new items from a home shopping channel. With help from family and friends we began the difficult task of sorting all this stuff to determine what we could sell and what needed to be disposed of. My wife tried to get QVC to take back many of these unopened, brand new items, but they refused. Their policy was returns accepted only 60 days from the date of purchase, even though they were still actively selling the items in question. There were hundreds of jewelry and clothing purchases, as well as a myriad of household items and gadgets. Some of this was fine jewelry, 14K still in the boxes. Hundreds of brand-new cookbooks were donated to our local public library.

The husband of a couple we had befriended at church helped himself to some of my mother in law's jewelry, old silver coins and a Bose music system. Once we discovered the loss our local police department was contacted, but they were not able to recover these items. It was their word against ours, and the police told us there was not enough evidence to prosecute them. The police chief who lived across the street said that these people knew what they were doing and must have had some experience with theft in their past. The music system alone was valued at around $500. Other family that were helping us sort through the items remembered the man eyeing the aged coins and some of the fine jewelry the day before they went missing. As if the whole situation wasn't bad enough already, we now had to deal with the feeling of being violated by people we had trusted. We were terribly upset and hurt by this situation but had to continue getting her house ready to be sold and preparing for the trip to Baltimore.

A few days before we were scheduled to leave for Baltimore, Johns Hopkins called to confirm my appointment with a radiation oncologist—not the specialization I needed for my situation. We did not know how the error occurred, but our flights and hotel were already booked, and we prayed I would still be able to get into another doctor with just a few days' notice. Instead of seeing the doctor on Monday, 08/27/12, as had been planned, they were able to schedule me with another oncologist for the next morning. Of course, that was the day of our flight departure, so we knew the morning would be hectic. Obviously, there was no other choice but to go with the trip and hope that the doctor would have the advice and recommendations I needed.

This situation left us with a free day to explore Baltimore. Instead of seeing the doctor on Monday, we did sight-seeing and shopping during the day. As we sat at the Inner Harbor for lunch, I remembered back to another time we had visited Baltimore for my college roommate's wedding. Even though that had only been a few years ago, the stark contrast between our reasons for being in the city became so evident. It was much harder to enjoy the crab cakes knowing what was coming the next day. That evening we went to Camden Yards to watch the Orioles play the White Sox. Since we both love baseball, the distraction was welcome given the incredible stress of the past month.

Tuesday morning, we checked out and decided to walk to Johns Hopkins from the hotel in downtown Baltimore. On Google maps, it did not appear to be too far from our hotel, and we knew we'd be sitting a lot that day at the appointment, airports, and plane. To say we made the wrong decision was an understatement; we should have taken a taxi. It was a longer walk than we thought and dragging our baggage through downtown Baltimore on a Tuesday morning was not much fun. Our journey took us through some very questionable neighborhoods, and we were praying for our own safety as we walked amid many boarded-up buildings and sidewalk debris. With anxious hearts we still made it in plenty of time for our appointment with Dr. Douglas Gladstone and did not have to wait long in the waiting room. We explained we had an afternoon flight out and everyone there was very accommodating.

When the doctor came into the room and after introductions by all of us, he asked me why I was there. Thinking it was an odd question to ask, I told him my history and that I had chronic lymphocytic leukemia. He then acted a little perturbed and said, "No, what type of cancer do you have?" At this point, I was getting agitated, because it appeared the appointment was with a doctor who was not understanding my condition. He had all my records in front of him, and when he asked again, I clearly told him I had CLL (chronic lymphocytic leukemia). What was the need to repeat this?? Did he even bother to read my records?? A fleeting thought that we had traveled half-way across the country for naught crossed my mind.

He then corrected me by saying that I had "IGVH Unmutated CLL with a 13q deletion." Stating that I just had CLL was apparently too generic for him. He wanted to be specific because this sub-type was why the chemotherapy was not keeping it in remission. Fortunately, at that point his demeanor changed, and he told us he would fully explain.

He gave us a copy of a medical journal study that he completed on this specific type of CLL and told us that the average life span of someone diagnosed with this was five years. FIVE years. So much for my *crock pot* leukemia. Even though what I had was *chronic* leukemia, the unmutated and 13q deletion factors transformed this to a very urgent situation. Since I had been diagnosed three years ago with this type of CLL, this meant, according to his study, I had only two years left to live.

Obviously, I appreciated his frankness and explanation of the situation, but Joyce and I sat there in the room in stunned silence. While we were extremely grateful that God had engineered this appointment with a guy that literally wrote the book (or at least a study) on my specific type of leukemia, the outcome he described shook us to the core.

Dr. Gladstone recommended that I get an allogeneic stem cell transplant as soon as possible. This type of transplant uses stem cells from a donor whose tissue type closely matches mine. Prior to getting this stem cell transplant, the existing leukemia cells would have to be knocked down to less than 20% of my white blood cells (currently they are 90%), and then my original immune system would have to be wiped out (overall white blood cell count down to 0) to allow the injected donor's stem cells to create new bone marrow in my body and eventually produce all of my red, white and platelet blood cells. He also stated that the mortality rate for this type of stem cell transplant is extremely high (50% or greater), but at Hopkins, it was closer to 25% because of the way they do it and the precautions they take. He was very direct and to the point and stated that we should come to Johns Hopkins to maximize my chances of survival. However, he also stated the risks of getting a stem cell (aka bone marrow) transplant from a donor included chronic life-long health issues due to my body trying to reject the new stem cells, marrow and blood as well as not surviving the procedure. I inquired whether he thought waiting was at all a possibility? Perhaps more or different chemo? Because my leukemia had come back with a vengeance, and the leukemia cells now made up almost 90% of my total bone marrow, I was now a Stage IV CLL patient and any waiting or further chemo treatments would only be a stopgap measure to delay the inevitable. It was either an allogeneic stem cell transplant or two years left of life. We told him we would consult further with Dr. Wade at home and would be in touch.

The taxi ride to the airport was indescribable. I am not sure what I expected to hear from this doctor, but up until today, *checking out* permanently and quickly was never mentioned. The urgency of the situation now became the focal point in my quest to live. I did not have many years to deal with the progression of this type of leukemia. Although it was classified as chronic, the characteristics were aggressive, and my options were to have this type of stem cell transplant or die soon.

We were both stunned as to the severity of my health condition and the high risks of lifelong problems that can occur with this type of stem cell transplant. As we waited for our connection to Chicago, Joyce and I re-read his study that gave me only one medical option for survival. All the way home on the multiple flights and connections, Joyce cried pretty much the whole time and I just got through the travel day in a state of shock and feeling numb. Neither of us has ever shied away from facing the reality of this battle, but today the war escalated on a grand scale. To make matters worse, the connection from Philadelphia to Chicago was delayed causing us to miss the last flight to Decatur thus needing to spend the night in Chicago. We called our daughter Jodi, who lived near the airport, and she joined us for dinner at a restaurant near O'Hare.

We broke the news to her and called several of the rest of the family members who were anxious to hear how my appointment went. Each retelling of the story solidified the reality of what was going to happen and what would happen if I did nothing. After spending the unplanned overnight in the Chicago area, we were able to make it home first thing the following morning. As soon as we arrived home, the urgencies of running our businesses took over, diverting our thoughts away momentarily from this unbelievable trip. Somehow, I hoped the doctor was wrong and the folks at Siteman Cancer Center in St. Louis would give me another viable option.

We had a family wedding to attend in the Chicago area that weekend, and a good part of our car travel was spent discussing everything we had been told by Dr. Gladstone. The thought of "wintering" in the Northeast was not something either of us felt would be feasible with our business and family obligations. Surely there was another way and the appointment in St. Louis was just days away.

The Tuesday after the Labor Day holiday was September 4, 2012, and we were both eager to find out what options St. Louis could offer. After labs, I was introduced to Dr. Peter Westervelt at 10:00AM. His perspective on my case was the same as Dr. Gladstone, and he recommended an allogeneic stem cell (or bone marrow) transplant as soon as possible. Clearly this procedure would be my only option; the only decision remaining was where I would have it done.

We got back home late that afternoon and I had band

practice at church that night for the upcoming weekend services. I was glad to have these activities to keep me from focusing totally on my dire health condition. This was a very strange situation for me. I did not *feel* sick and was able to function without any difficulties, but these doctors were telling me that without an allogeneic stem cell transplant, I would not be alive in two years. The flip side was that getting the transplant had extreme risks up to and including dying during the treatments and transplant. Both Dr. Gladstone and Dr. Westervelt agreed that I should have a "reduced intensity transplant," so that aspect helped a little.

In a traditional allogeneic stem cell transplant, the patient is given large doses of chemo and whole-body radiation to knock the cancer back and kill off the existing bone marrow. While the doctors said they would probably not be able to take out all the existing cancer, the goal was to knock it back to less than 20% so that the new cells would not have such a large army to go up against. It was also vital that my old bone marrow would be *killed off* so that the new cells from my donor could be completely ingrafted. Because of new medical procedures (some of which Dr. Gladstone helped to pioneer), I could do the reduced intensity transplant which would not include the radiation to my body. I was told the chemo would be like what I had already received and would take several months to complete. During this time, we would be actively seeking a donor from the Be the Match data bank in case family members were ineligible.

Armed with all this information, we met with Dr. Wade at our local cancer center the day after the St. Louis appointment. Dr. Wade shared with us that shortly before I started chemotherapy in June 2010, my case was one of several cases that he reviewed with a panel of doctors at Washington University/Siteman in St. Louis. He told us that this was done regularly since research was constantly changing treatment options and new studies were being started frequently. His hope then was that I might have a better option than the standard treatments. Back then one of the doctors at Washington University who looked at my type of CLL suggested an allogeneic stem cell transplant because of the aggressive factors both other doctors cited.

Because I had chronic, not acute leukemia, my health insurance would not pay for an allogeneic stem cell transplant initially, regardless of the sub-type I had. They would only pay for a transplant if I relapsed, which of course I did, and sooner than anyone expected. Dr. Wade also emphasized the fact that once the donor's stem cells are infused into my body, there is no removing them if there are serious rejection issues. What a decision to face! I was between a rock and a hard place, but all three oncologists agreed—an allogeneic stem cell transplant was my only medical option.

With Joyce having to take care of her mother who was still adjusting to her new life in assisted living and managing our home-based garment business, Johns Hopkins was too far away to work for us. We also checked out both facilities online and found similar ratings and reviews for them, so I felt like either choice would be fine to get this done. The <25% mortality rate at Hopkins sounded more favorable, but Dr. Wade assured us that any of the "High Volume" transplant centers in the US have similar outcomes. Barnes Hospital in St. Louis also fell into that category.

The more we discussed the pros and cons, it became obvious that Johns Hopkins was too far away and was difficult to get to even by plane because of the many connections between Central Illinois and Baltimore. Winters in the northeast are notoriously wicked, and St. Louis was a two-and-a-half-hour car ride. Both places offered the identical procedure, and the decision was made to proceed with the allogeneic stem cell transplant at Siteman Cancer Center at Barnes Hospital in St. Louis. The months ahead would now have a tangible blueprint for my survival. The circumstances of life in those next few months had a way of blurring the lines a bit.

Look Up

Chapter 5

Allogeneic Stem Cell Transplant Prep (Sep 2012 – Jan 2013)

So how does someone proceed with getting an allogeneic stem cell (bone marrow) transplant? All I could remember from having talked with other people who had family or friends that had done this is that it was an awfully long and awfully expensive ordeal. For me, the first step was to get my health insurance approval to pay for this. The team of people working with us at both Cancer Care in Decatur and Siteman in St. Louis knew what needed to be done. I was even provided a "Transplant Coordinator" at Siteman who would be my go-to person for anything associated with the transplant. After relapsing and getting three oncologists agreeing that a bone marrow transplant was needed, my health insurance approved this procedure and also assigned me a transplant coordinator to be my point of contact. I knew this had to be a major deal if they were going to devote a single person out of such large organizations to handle my case personally.

The next thing I learned was the leukemia had to be knocked back to remission levels of 10-20% or the transplant would not work. As of the most recent sample, my bone marrow was 90% leukemia. The doctor explained that once the new stem cells are put in my body they are like seedlings. It will take a bit of time for them to create my new bone marrow and overtake my old bone marrow, and the army of cancer cells they must face needs to be small for them to successfully do this. At the same time, they will also be "taking over" my bone marrow. If my donor had a different blood type than I had, the transplant would cause my blood type to change to whatever the donor had. To do this (they call the process *chimerism*) my old bone marrow must be almost completely obliterated so that the old cannot fight off the new. Talk about freakish!! And of course, the vehicle by which all this would occur was more chemo and harsher drugs given as preparation.

I still had the Power Port in my chest from 2010, so by the middle of September 2012 I got the first of four monthly rounds of chemo to be administered by the local cancer care center using two CLL targeted medications. Rituxin, which was used in 2010, and a new chemo, Bendomustine, were infused through my Power Port on September 17, 2012, and the next day I got just Bendomustine. Getting both chemo drugs on the same day took most of the day and the single chemo took half a day to administer. Although I felt no nausea, I was extremely fatigued after these first two sessions of Round 1. Feeling like this was not what I was hoping for, but it was better than the chemo I received in 2010 where I had to get five days in a row for each round.

Even though it was only two days, my vitals had to be

closely monitored to ensure that red, white, and platelet blood cells would remain high enough to allow me to endure the difficult transplant process. All my organ functions were also watched to assure I had the strength needed.

Dr. Wade also told me to gain 15 to 20 pounds prior to the allogeneic stem cell transplant because he said that I did not have enough reserves to get through it. When I asked him why, he said the week before the transplant is very grueling and the meds I would be given to "kill off" my old bone marrow would cause extreme nausea and diarrhea causing me to drop a lot of weight very quickly. As I mentioned earlier, I worked out regularly and had a healthy diet to keep myself in good physical shape. For me to put on that much weight in just four months was not an easy task to accomplish. I loathed (and still do) the taste of protein powder in drinks, but Joyce tried to make them more palatable by blending in fresh fruit. Dr. Wade suggested things like more mashed potatoes and ice cream; so, for four months, I ate large quantities of food that I normally would eat sparingly.

And of course, we had to find a donor. My only living sibling is my older brother, who when tested did not prove to be a match. I have two daughters, but the doctors were concerned that any genetic aspect of this may have been passed to them and perhaps their marrow did not contain the "x-factor" needed to eradicate the leukemia.

Be-the-Match, operated by the National Marrow Donor Program, manages the largest and most diverse marrow registry in the world. Barnes contacted them, and through their computer analysis of my DNA, four possible matches out of 14 million people in the registry were found. Their transplant personnel recommended getting full testing done on two of these four initial matches because to do each one individually would take too much time, in case the first one was not a match. The registry only stores limited information on each donor. I also found out the extended testing can be cost prohibitive, as this would be over $9,000 per donor candidate. This testing was vital to pick the most compatible donor for me, but unfortunately, my health insurance would not pay for the matched unrelated donor (MUD) extended testing. I did get some financial aid in the search but did not in the full testing. My transplant coordinator said she would continue working on other avenues to try and get financial help with these necessary tests that my insurance did not cover. I found it interesting that the costs for the search and the testing needed to assure a proper match were outside the realms of my coverage.

This was going to be a big ordeal in so many ways. We needed all the support from the medical people, but also our family and friends. In order to keep our support network of people up to date and allow an easier way to get my current health status out, Joyce got me set up on CaringBridge.org, a website for people like me going through a major medical crisis. This allows a one stop place for us to post updates and people to respond with encouraging notes. If someone did not want to type a note, they could show their support by posting a heart symbol. This became a crucial communication link for me to receive the emotional support from family and friends as I continued through this very uncertain and difficult process that would require me to be isolated for extended times.

At the end of September, which was my mother's 82nd birthday, I was again at our local cancer care center getting another blood draw and checkup with my local oncologist, Dr. Wade. My blood counts looked good and the first round of chemo was kicking the leukemia down already.

With this good report, Joyce and I went the next weekend to Indiana to meet up with good friends that used to live here back in the 1990s. We thought that we needed to get some fun weekends away while we could before my body's immune system would be so weakened by the treatments that we could not be out much or around other people. Spending time with other people was good for my mental and emotional well- being. Knowing that our friends were Christians, the prayer support was always well received.

Since becoming a Christian in New York in 1984, I had read and studied the Bible frequently to grow in my knowledge and relationship with Jesus Christ through understanding God's word and applying it to my life. I regularly attended and participated in church services and Bible classes and learned from others about how God worked in their lives. Developing these relationships with other Christians and my desire to grow closer to Jesus through the Spirit had brought me to a place where my main life goal was to live daily in His will for me.

Trying to grow deeper spiritually and listening inwardly for God to speak to me was not an easy process, but I had already experienced multiple times in the past where He was able to guide and direct my decisions and give me an inner peace and joy that are hard to explain. Being with other believers and having them also pray with us and for us brought more of the sense of God's presence into my serious health situation. Given the gravity of what I was facing, I needed His guidance and presence in me more than ever to keep a positive attitude and to not get negative and depressed. The tangible touch of being with friends and sharing these burdens truly lightened the load.

At the time I was really feeling good and being able to enjoy life was something I was not going to miss out on. I had another checkup on October 3, 2012 that showed my blood counts were still doing well, so we planned another weekend trip the middle of the month to Southern Illinois to enjoy the fall color and local wineries there. It was comforting to hear from our friends on this bus trip that I "looked good" because they knew I was going through chemo again. One of the difficult parts of the cancer journey is looking in the mirror and realizing you look pale, gaunt, and sick. I still was having some fatigue, but it was manageable, and I could still perform my daily activities.

My second round of chemo was on October 15 and 16, 2012. This round went pretty much like the first one. Prior to getting the second day of chemo, I was on-site at one of my computer customers that is located across the street from our local cancer care center. I was able to fix several computer issues and meet with the finance manager prior to getting the chemotherapy and afterwards, drive home with no ill effects. That entire week was good, and I continued with computer and garment work and even played piano at a senior living center.

My youngest daughter came to visit on October 23 from the Chicago area, and we took her to the Abraham Lincoln Museum in Springfield, Illinois. Since my blood counts were still high enough and I was feeling good, we wanted to get out and enjoy time with her. The Lincoln Museum is such a wonderful place, and the distraction from my treatment regimen was treasured.

After getting my mother-in-law's house ready to be sold during August and September, we had a single mom purchase it in October of that year. That had been a major concern for my wife because she was so busy dealing with our work and my treatments on top of this. What a huge load off us to complete this prior to my transplant. We really felt God's hand in the timing of all these things because we did not want to have to contend with a real estate sale in the middle of the transplant.

Joyce still had to manage her mother's care in the assisted living apartment, but Pauline was getting used to living there and starting to enjoy it. Integrating her into a new social scene and lifestyle was challenging, but Joyce made sure the staff there took care of her mom's needs. Pauline said having her breakfast delivered to her room each day was almost like having room service at a hotel daily. It was one of those little perks that helped her mom settle into her new surroundings.

Since I was Joyce's caregiver during her breast cancer battle, I knew all too well what she was dealing with and how hard it is to juggle all life's tasks on top of taking care of your spouse who cannot do much to help.

After playing piano the following weekend at church and getting another good report from a checkup with Dr. Wade at the end of the month, we had several of our church elders come to our home that evening and pray over me and Joyce anointing me with oil as the Bible teaches for my healing. I so much appreciated all of them coming and praying with and for us. Once again, I felt God's presence in our living room that evening which gave me inner peace facing the uncertain future. I already had experienced his intervention through how well I had endured all the previous chemotherapy treatments. Now that I was facing more chemotherapy and a bone marrow transplant, I pressed in harder to get closer to God.

The next day I was at a local dermatologist's office getting my body checked. The oncologists had recommended that this be done to ensure no skin issues were present prior to the allogeneic stem cell transplant. After the exam, we scheduled another appointment to get a dark mole removed from my back as a precaution.

My next trip scheduled to Siteman Cancer Center in St. Louis was in early November. We went down there on

Sunday, and spent Sunday and Monday looking at short term stay apartments in the St. Louis area. Because the risks and need for frequent check- ups is great during the time shortly after the transplant, Barnes requires that patients stay locally after they are discharged from the hospital in case any problems develop.

We looked at several furnished apartments, but some of the ones closest to the hospital had street parking and some of the neighborhoods were known to have a high crime rate. One complex south of the hospital had a very lovely apartment, but when Joyce googled the area, she found out a shooting/murder occurred at the complex just a couple of months prior. We decided to look a bit further out because Joyce would be traveling back to the apartment most days after dark, and safety was a concern with several of these places.

The other issue is that in November of 2012, none of the places had open availability. We were wise to do this search early and put our names on the waiting list. We eventually found a great furnished apartment near the Galleria off Brentwood Blvd. This place had gated covered parking, and the location was close to several convenient grocery stores and pharmacies. It was only a ten-minute drive to the hospital yet provided the convenience and safety we were searching. We were told that openings happen frequently and there should be an opening that we could secure with a month- to-month lease by the time we needed it.

During that same stay in St. Louis, I had a full day of

medical testing including an echo cardiogram and lab work, appointment with Dr. Westervelt, a bilateral bone marrow biopsy (more about this later) and a pulmonary function test. Dr. Westervelt was pleased with the progress from my first two rounds of chemotherapy and recommended getting the last two rounds prior to the transplant which was scheduled for mid-January 2013. These heart and lung tests were required to insure I did not have any other health issues that could cause problems during the allogeneic stem cell transplant process. My healthy lifestyle prior to all this was paying off, because having pre-existing issues like heart disease or diabetes could complicate this process greatly. Fortunately, I had none.

During a regular bone marrow biopsy one side of your hip is drilled on the back side and bone marrow aspirated out. This device looks a bit like a wine-bottle corkscrew, and the technician must generate enough force to screw this tool down into the bone and then reverse the process to extract the marrow. A bilateral bone marrow biopsy is where both sides of the hips get drilled and aspirated. Not only did I have to endure that, but I also had a female trainee (Ashley) attempting to drill through my hard bones! She could not get enough force to get through my bone and I could feel her trainer (Greg) move her hand to get the device more perpendicular on my hip. Typically, one side would take about ten minutes for the entire procedure. Ashley could not generate enough momentum to get through my bone and I was starting to feel her digging into me. After giving me more local anesthetic shots to numb me up again, Greg took over and got both sides done. It took nearly 45 minutes to complete the entire process, and I was sorer from this bone marrow biopsy than from previous ones.

The best news from this trip overshadowed the pain of the biopsies. Doctor told me that the two people that underwent initial testing from Be-The-Match bone marrow registry were both good matches for me! One was a male and one a female who recently had a baby. Since she just had a baby, the doctor recommended the male first; however, they recommended doing the full testing on both people because if the first person does not make it through the vetting process, the second person is a backup that can be used to keep me on schedule for mid-January 2013. Since I could not get financial assistance for the $18K in testing fees, I reviewed my medical insurance policy and saw where they would cover all costs for my donor. I began working with my insurance transplant coordinator and stated that if we use one of these persons for my transplant, shouldn't my insurance company cover testing for my actual donor? The lady there was helpful, and she agreed that should be the case and would take steps to see if we could be reimbursed the costs for the actual donor.

It seemed like that time in my life was just one medical appointment after another. Two days after spending what seemed like an eternity doing medical testing in St Louis, I was back in Decatur getting an EKG and chest X-Ray. I saw Dr. Wade on Friday, November 9, to review the results of all my recent testing and confirm my third round of chemotherapy scheduled for the following week. I had also gained 10 pounds so far thanks to my wife's great cooking and protein shakes. I got to the point where I could not tolerate the nasty taste of the whey protein anymore and delved into extra ice cream to try and gain additional weight. From the biopsies, it was determined my leukemia had dropped to 12-15% of my bone marrow which was a good level to be at with two more rounds of chemo to go. Round three of chemotherapy went the same as the other two, but now I was starting to experience some digestive issues as a result of this round. As a precaution, I got a CT scan immediately after round three of chemotherapy. Then on November 20, I got another blood test and reviewed the CT scans with Dr. Wade's nurse practitioner. Fortunately, everything was fine, and my stomach problems were just a result of the intense chemo I been taking for the last several weeks.

The next week I went back to the skin doctor and had the dark mole removed from my back. She explained that there would be some discomfort and I told her "don't worry about it." Removing a mole using a local anesthetic is nothing compared to the bone marrow biopsies. The following week she removed the stitches. Fortunately, it was just a benign growth, and I could check one more thing off the list of pre-transplant to-dos.

One of my other to-do's was to find a resource to cover my computer customers while I was unavailable. In fact, I did not know if I would ever be able to work on computers after the transplant. While I was hopeful, I also knew the incredible risks I was facing. I contacted a local company that sold and supported PCs for small businesses, and they agreed to cover my computer clients for me while I was out. I was able to get all my computer customers entered in their sales system the first week of December.

This was so hard for me to do since I had done computer work for many of these local small businesses for over 15 years. I had been transparent with my customers about my health situation, and they were very gracious and understanding about my upcoming transplant. By letting these people know what was happening, they provided me more encouragement and support on top of my family and close friends. I really appreciated this. My recommendation to anyone going through a major health challenge is to let people around you know about it. Do not try to cover it up and be silent. Let others in to help you get through it. I have always been a giver, and it was a process for me to allow others to do the giving. By being transparent with my customers, I was able to receive daily encouragement that I needed as the time for the transplant was closing in rapidly.

The final round of chemotherapy at our local cancer center began on December 10, 2012. As I had experienced before in 2010, the cumulative effect of multiple rounds of chemotherapy was felt and my digestive issues continued. I began taking a daily probiotic to help with those issues, and fortunately, I did not pick up any other illness during this time. I had to be completely healthy in other ways to be ready for the upcoming bone marrow transplant. Joyce also was able to avoid the usual colds and flu that typically start this time of year. Once again, prayer works!

One unusual and a little disturbing aspect came to our attention in mid-December. We were told they were having difficulty getting responses from my donor, and so the transplant check in date was moved to January 21, 2013 with the actual transplant at the end of January rather than the middle of the month. We asked if the donor was having second thoughts about being a donor but were assured that was not the case and that he was, in fact, enthusiastic about being able to donate stem cells for me. However, because of the delay, the testing he needed to do for infectious diseases was delayed slightly, causing the overall delay of the process. Fortunately, he passed all the testing.

Given that my donor was now confirmed, I again contacted my health insurance transplant coordinator and asked that they cover the testing fees that had been done on my donor. After several correspondence efforts with her, we were able to secure reimbursement for the person who would be my donor. We would still have to pay $9K for the woman that was also tested, but that is much better than having to pay $18K for both.

We were now a little over one month out and the reality of this was really setting in. Being December, I had extra piano engagements for Christmas parties and church. I was able to play them and again not get any illnesses. I also spent additional time with family and friends during the holidays. Our work schedule was normal through this time also which helped me not dwell on the upcoming St. Louis event. The normal daily distractions kept me from focusing on the huge endeavor that I was about to undertake. That year there was a lot of talk about the Mayan calendar that stopped on December 21, 2012. Many people speculated it could be the end of the world on that date and given what I was facing in 2013, I was secretly hoping they might be right.

By playing piano at many nursing homes and senior assisted living centers for 20 years, I had become friends with several residents and had gotten close to a couple of them. Dee was a delightful Christian woman that I would always wheel back to her room after completing my piano playing at her nursing home. This brave soul had been bed ridden with MS for 38 years and so I paid a local massage therapist to give her treatments to give her some comfort. Although she was unable to do anything except be in bed, she always had a smile and a positive word when I saw her. She passed away close to Christmas 2012, and I went to her visitation just before the New Year.

Margaret, a resident at a Springfield senior assisted living center that I had gotten close to after years of playing piano, also died in early January 2013. These two ladies were my closest friends in these facilities, and they had told me that they were praying for my healing from this leukemia. I thought what wonderful people they were for being concerned for me when they were in their own difficult health situations. In the back of my mind I found myself wondering if I was next on the list to go. I struggled daily then with thoughts of my own mortality and the uncertainty of what would happen.

Well, the world did not end in December, so by January

2013 we prepared for the move to St. Louis. It started with another CT scan in Decatur and then down to St. Louis on January 6 to get more testing done including blood work and another bone marrow biopsy to see how much leukemia was left after four rounds of chemotherapy. It was down to less than 10% of my bone marrow which was great for the upcoming transplant. The doctor again explained that the army of new stem cell seedlings needed to battle as few leukemia cells as possible in order to eradicate the disease. A target was less than 20% leukemia, and I was below that. The pre-transplant chemo had done what it was supposed to do.

We were then notified that the donor would not agree to having his hip drilled for bone marrow in case the *pheresis* (filtering of stem cells collected via IV) did not provide enough stem cells. This delayed my allogeneic stem cell transplant to February 6, because they might have to do multiple days of IV stem cell collection and running my donor's blood through the filter to extract stem cells. This was not a big deal to me since he was still going through with the donation. Initially we thought the donor had to have the hip drill done to extract the marrow, just as I had done. Fortunately, they can collect the cells by doing an ordinary blood donation and then filtering out all the cells except for the stem cells. Those would be used for my transplant. And as you will read shortly, the delay worked out better for us. I completed the last of the medical testing with an echo and lung function test on 01/18/13 and was ready physically for the transplant.

Barnes personnel were very up front about the huge risks of getting an allogeneic stem cell transplant, and we transferred money from a CD that had matured to our savings account for Joyce to use if needed. I was thankful to God that we had enough finances for Joyce in case I did not survive this procedure or was incapacitated for a long period of time afterwards. It was stressful enough going through this without having to be concerned about enough money to get bills paid.

However, during the month of January 2013, our family experienced several other traumatic events.

On the evening of Saturday January 5, we received a call that my then 82-year-old mother had a stroke and was hospitalized. At a Barnes and Noble bookstore in Springfield, Illinois she began to feel ill and so drove herself back home. She decided perhaps a bath might help her, and once she got into the tub, she was unable to get back out. Fortunately, she had called for help and my nephew assisted in getting her to the hospital. This was in the middle of a huge mid-winter flu outbreak, and my brother Gary told me not to come to the hospital for fear of contracting something that could derail the transplant. We communicated via phone, and it was determined to be a mild stroke, so they kept her in the hospital an additional day for observation.

We decided to have a "send-off" party for me on the January 13. Again, with so much uncertainty in the future, I wanted to be able to see all my close friends and family before this huge life altering event. We told everyone it was vital that they come only if they were "healthy." Everyone assured us they were all well and we had a wonderful time talking and taking photos. Joyce created a "Team Larry" logo and made some tee shirts for all of them to wear. It was great to be able to see so many of those I cared about so much all at one time. This little party was a great encouragement and a respite for the situations that were soon coming our way. Although my mom was not up to making this trip, I did get to spend time with other family members.

On Sunday January 20, just one week before we were to head to St. Louis, we got another disturbing evening call. My mother-in-law (then 95) had fallen at her assisted living facility and was being transferred to the ER. We found out that she had in fact fallen twice that day. The first time was mid-morning when she fell in her bathroom which apparently caused the first fracture to her tailbone. Because of the pain she was in, she again fell while trying to walk to dinner that evening and received a hairline fracture in her hip. Because once again I did not want to expose myself to any flu viruses, Joyce met the ambulance at the ER, and we communicated via phone.

My poor mother-in-law spent 9.5 hours on a gurney before it was determined that she had these fractures and needed to be admitted. What was not determined was that she also had a serious UTI which may have weakened her and caused the falls to begin with. The fractures were not serious enough to require surgery, but she was now unable to pull herself up from a chair or bed. By late in the day after her discharge, she had gone nearly 24 hours without voiding, and the facility recommended sending her again to the hospital because she was also now feverish and in serious pain from both the UTI and the two fractures. The place she lived in did not offer services for either lifting or catheter bag management, and it was becoming obvious that she might need skilled nursing care. Because we did not feel comfortable sending her back to the same hospital that missed the UTI from the start, we had her transported to another hospital on the other side of town from where we lived. It was now Tuesday evening, and the trip to St. Louis to begin my transplant was only a week away.

Joyce shared that the instant the catheter was inserted, enough urine was extracted to nearly fill a large catheter bag. The ER staff there said she had a "raging UTI," and with the circumstances of the two fractures, she never should have been discharged from the other facility two days prior. Their plan was to get the UTI under control, begin some light therapy for the fractures, and get her pain under control. In addition, we were told there was NO WAY she could return to the assisted living community she had just come to enjoy because she indeed would require skilled nursing care.

The very next day, we received yet another unbelievable call—my oldest daughter had just been robbed at gunpoint at her home. To say Joyce and I were in a state of disbelief at the series of events that had transpired this month was a vast understatement. Amy, who did hair out of her home salon, said she went to answer the door and a man with a gun forced his way in demanding money. She had a client in the chair at the time, and our four-year-old granddaughter was at home as well.

The culprit forced them upstairs and made them lie face down on the bed. We all surmised that he apparently was at the wrong house because he was looking for large sums of cash and Amy obviously did not have anything like that there. The next several days we followed her journey as she picked someone out of a lineup that she thought was the assailant but had an alibi for the date and time. About a week later the actual person was arrested after trying a similar tactic in another neighborhood. We were so blessed that they were both ok given the gravity of the situation. Joyce and her mother watched the story from the hospital room on the TV that night. Another incredible intervention by the Lord kept our loved ones safe.

We had planned to leave for St. Louis around 3:30 am on the morning of January 30, 2013. The entire day before was spent packing the things we felt we would immediately need and tending to Pauline, who was being discharged from the hospital. Joyce had to move her to a nursing home because of the physical state she was now in. Although the antibiotics cleared up her UTI, the doctors surmised the fractures may be keeping her from being able to void naturally. She left the hospital with a catheter bag, and no one had any idea when that would be able to be removed.

Fortunately, her senior assisted living center was affiliated with a nursing home less than a mile from our house. Joyce's poor mom was now in a state of upheaval once again and as an only child, all the responsibility for this move fell on Joyce to try and relocate her mom as we were planning our own temporary relocation. At 4 pm on January 29, the final paperwork was signed to admit Pauline to the nursing home. Joyce was able to gather some of her personal belongings from her assisted living apartment, and we both hoped this would only be a temporary stay at the nursing home. For now, though, her very mobile mom was confined to bed with fractures and a catheter bag. It was horrible to see the anguish my wife was going through as she attempted to juggle all the balls that were now in her hands.

The most positive thing about everything that happened was that the process for me had been delayed until the end of the month. If the transplant had happened as originally planned for mid-January, we would have been trying to manage many of these things remotely. It also gave me time to have lunches with several of my close Christian friends who prayed for and encouraged me greatly. Our Caring Bridge website kept family and friends up to date on my status. They posted many encouraging messages and let us know we were in their thoughts and prayers. This was another key for Joyce and me to get through this difficult time and our sustenance during these exceedingly difficult days.

On January 29, around 5:30pm, the physician assistant from Barnes Hospital called with the news that I had to have fasting bloodwork done no later than 8:00AM on January 30, not noon as we were first told. If it were done any later than that, we were told it would delay the entire process. The patient advocate that was supposed to inform us of this scheduling change had been out sick, and no one got around to calling us sooner. We debated on when to leave, since our original plan was not viable.

We did not get much sleep that night and got on the highway at 3:00 am on January 30, 2013 to drive to St. Louis for the journey for which God had paved the way. The weather was horrible the night before with heavy pouring rain and thunderstorms because it got close to 70 degrees the previous day. That is NOT normal for Illinois at the end of January. Fortunately, at that time in the wee hours of the morning, there was sparse traffic on the highways.

What awaited me, and whether I would ever see my home again were tucked in the back of my mind as I crossed the Mississippi and glanced at the illuminated St. Louis Gateway Arch. The moment for the main battle against this invader had arrived.

The time for my healing from cancer was about to begin.

Chapter 6

Allogeneic Stem Cell Transplant (Jan 2013 – Feb 2013)

Once we crossed the river, we drove to the massive parking garage that housed the vehicles of patients and visitors at the huge Center for Advanced Medicine (CAM) at Barnes Hospital. The garage was basically empty, and when we pulled in, we said a prayer in the car before proceeding to the lab which opened at 6 am. I could not have anything by mouth seven hours prior to the 2 pm installation of the Hickman tri-fusion port and anesthesia at Barnes Hospital, so I wanted to allow enough time to get the lab work done as well as have breakfast. I was the first person in line at the seventh-floor lab. When I had been there before, it was always later in the day with dozens of people waiting to get lab work done. It was a little unnerving to realize that many people were battling cancer. But on this day, I stood alone as other folks trickled in behind me. The tech took the needed blood, and we had nearly 45 minutes to spare before my 7 am "nothing by mouth before anesthesia" cutoff.

Just a couple of blocks from the facility was an Einstein's

Bagels that had just opened for the day. Joyce and I entered, and we ate a light breakfast as we sat alone in the restaurant quietly wondering how the rest of this day would go. We meandered back to the car, now aware that the rain had stopped, and the cold front was starting to move through. We were both extremely sleepy, and since I had no other procedures scheduled until my port insertion at 2 pm, we drove back to the parking garage and kicked the seats back to try and sleep a bit. We were awakened around 9 am as the sounds of vehicles looking for parking and the slamming of car doors created a loud hum which broke the silence. This is a five-floor parking garage, and many cars would have to circle the facility multiple times to try and find that elusive spot. Because we were there so early, we captured a prime spot near the door.

We went to the large main lobby on the first floor and found two seats. Joyce had browsed numerous catalogs and magazines she had brought, and I rested in the chair for a while. Becoming anxious, I decided to explore the lobby a bit more. On the other side from where we were sitting was a beautiful grand piano that was available to be played. Somehow finding this piano at this very moment was a small blessing I could not have imagined. I began playing music around 10:30am that morning and continued all the way till nearly 12:30pm. So many people's faces lit up and thanked me in appreciation for my God-given talent. Then the thought hit me: would this be my final concert? The fun was over at 1:00pm when we headed upstairs to meet with Dr. Westervelt's nurse practitioner and get the final schedule. I thought, "I've heard of punt, pass, and kick, but this is cut, poke, and drill."

Hospital in-patient registration included some unusual questions. How much sick time was I allowed from my employer? I answered that I got all the sick time I wanted as well as all the vacation time I desired. The Barnes person asked me, "Who is your employer?" I smiled and said, "Me!" I made no income when not working; but because Joyce and I had managed our resources well for the past 23 years, we could weather this financial storm. I was also asked about having a will in place and if all my affairs were in order. Those are not the types of questions to put you at ease, but here we go....

When I had the surgery for the power port put in my right chest in June 2010 in Decatur, Illinois, I was extremely upset about coming to terms with the reality of the cancer and had a very difficult time dealing with that surgical procedure. I know I was not the model patient that day, but by now I had grown accustomed to getting stuck and drilled by medical personnel. What a difference that last two plus years had made in me! I was not nervous at all getting this Hickman tri-fusion port surgically inserted in my left chest. In fact, a little after 1:30pm we were in the interventional radiology prep area and I was looking forward to getting this over and done with.

Prior to being put under anesthesia, I was laughing with the nurses and very relaxed. Unlike the power port, which is completely placed under the skin, this tri-fusion device had three connectors that were outside my body. This was needed for the transplant because the single line of my power port was not large enough to accommodate everything associated with this procedure. I was glad that this port did not require getting stuck through the skin every time it is accessed, but it had to be covered with saran wrap so I could shower. This one connected to my jugular vein on the left side of my neck. I looked like a cyborg robot with all this hardware in me on both the left and right sides of my chest. I was to report to the infusion area next, to begin the week-long prep that would "kill off" the rest of my bone marrow production to prepare a clean slate for the new stem cells that would be infused.

We arrived in this area a little after 4 pm, and the nurses ushered us to a large back room where multiple people were getting different types of chemo. I was supposed to be there by 3:00, and we asked the people in anesthesia to please let infusion know I was running late. Apparently, they did not because one of the nurses commented that she was not sure I was even on the premises. We apologized for the delay, but it was not within my power to get there sooner because I was in recovery longer than they anticipated.

I got Rituxan chemo for my first round of prep meds in the infusion area. Because I had Rituxan before, I was not too concerned about side effects since I really did not have many with this drug when I had taken it before. However, the process here seemed to drag out substantially, with long waits between the time I was in my seat to when the pre-meds were administered. These drugs are a cocktail of sedatives and antihistamines given to counteract any nausea that might ensue from the chemo drugs. By now it was near 6 pm, and Joyce and I were both getting hungry. I was told I could have food, and there was a sandwich shop within walking distance of this building. Joyce went there to get us some light sandwiches, and I was still hooked up and getting chemo after 7:00.

Because of the confusion and delays, Joyce went up to the fifth floor where I would be checking in. She wanted to let them know I was here, but the chemo was taking longer than anticipated. They told her my room was not quite ready yet but should be within the hour. Once again, they expressed surprise because, apparently, they did not know I had checked in either. I must say that this was a bit unnerving since I assumed their computer networks would show that I had checked in at my various stops.

Finally, around 8:00 pm, I was wheeled up to the fifth floor in the Schoenberg Pavilion which is connected to the CAM. This is the hospital part of the building but has walkways and elevators that all connect. Again, someone commented that they were not sure if I was still going to be there, but I was there several hours later than planned due to no fault of mine. The 31 single occupant rooms on this floor are designed for bone marrow transplant patients containing a controlled environment that filters the air to minimize exposure to airborne illnesses and are kept sanitized. There is limited visitation to also reduce the patients' exposure to getting sick. Hospital staff are specially trained to care for stem cell transplant patients with higher levels of staffing. A very pleasant nurse arrived in my room around 9 pm and wrote several things on the white board posted on the wall in the room opposite my bed.

The room itself was large and I was at the far end of the hallway in a corner away from the nurses' station (which was noisy) and the elevators. The adjustable bed was against the wall, and a large recliner chair and floor lamp were next to it. A small desk with another chair was in the corner, near the windows, which overlooked the street below and a beautiful church across the street. My closet was also roomy, with cabinets above and drawers below it—something like a built-in armoire. A large sink with cabinets below it and a large mirror above was located on the opposite side of the bed with the bathroom on the other side of that. The shower and the toilet both had safety bars. Larger than most standard hospital bathrooms indicated the whole set-up was designed for extended stays. We carefully placed a grocery cart full of my personal belongings in my new closet.

As I had been going through these treatments, I always signed up for clinical trials so my treatments could be used as information to help people in the future. This was not different when getting the transplant, and I had already signed up for another clinical trial study. In 2012, a new reduced intensity stem cell transplant preparation protocol had been approved (thanks to Dr. Gladstone that I saw at Johns Hopkin) and I was in a clinical trial associated with refining this procedure.

I had been assigned to Arm 1 in this study which had a

less severe prep regiment than Arm 2. My hometown oncologist, Dr. Wade, had told me that being in Arm 1 of the study was better than Arm 2 because the ATG meds used in Arm 2 were very rough. But on the night of my check-in when the nurse was writing on the white board, she wrote "Arm 2" on the board. When I inquired, she described the medications that were to be given over these next seven days to prepare my body to receive the new stem cells, and Arm 2 medications were going to be administered. We assured her I was to be in Arm 1 of the study, and after all the confusion with scheduling earlier in the day, I was really in no mood for further mix-ups. Since it was so late by then, she advised us that she would have my doctor address this in the morning.

Because Joyce has ongoing cervical issues, she could not sleep properly in the recliner in the room. Our apartment was not going to be ready until February 7, so Joyce had a room booked at a Holiday Inn Express nearby and headed there after ten that night. Now the uncertainty of the prep meds I was going to get were in question, and Doctor Wade had warned that the Arm 2 meds were nothing I wanted to have to deal with. Reflecting on this first exceptionally long day and trying to get accustomed to these new surroundings prevented much sleep that night.

I was still pondering this the next morning when Joyce arrived back bright and early. Dr. Westervelt, my oncologist at Barnes Hospital that was directing this transplant procedure, came in shortly thereafter. He explained that he had a change of heart and put me in Arm 2 of the study because he was concerned that since I was young (relatively speaking) and in good health with a strong immune system, my body could reject the transplant using the Arm 1 preparation medications. The stronger Arm 2 medications were going to be used to knock my immune system down enough to allow the transplant to work. I did not like this change but Doctor Westervelt told me that if my immune system was not sufficiently eradicated, I might have to go through this whole process again. Since I did not want the possibility of repeating this process, the Arm 2 medications became the regimen for me.

On Thursday afternoon, I received my first infusion of the ATG (Anti-thymocyte globulin which is used to reduce rejection after an allogeneic stem cell transplant) which took six hours coming through my tri-fusion port. When Dr. Wade said that this would be rough, he was not exaggerating. While getting this, I experienced body shakes and pain and fever. These were enhanced body shakes, what the staff called *rigors* and from what Joyce described, I almost looked as though I was having a seizure. When she rang for the nurse, she came in almost immediately and gave me a shot of Demerol to calm the shaking. She told me this reaction was to be expected since my body is going to try and fight off anything that is put into it. Now this really caused me displeasure with my body, since it was not fighting off the leukemia cancer which is what it should have been doing in the first place! Fortunately, the Demerol *rescue* meds helped alleviate these issues. This was far worse than any chemo treatments that I had experienced before. This was Day -6 with the countdown to Day 0

(Transplant Day) on February 6, 2013. All I could think of it "Oh boy, I get five more days of this *prep.*"

The next two days I got Fludarabine and Cytoxan chemo meds in the morning, then good old ATG for six hours each afternoon into the evening. These first few days in the hospital were also difficult not only from the physical reactions, but I also could not sleep much from hospital staff checking my vital signs, drawing blood, and having an uncomfortable bed. The mattress was rubbery and spongy and felt like an inflatable pool mattress. Even with the *rescue* meds, the ATG and chemo really took a toll on me which included constant low-grade fever, body aches and pains, and upper and lower GI issues around the clock. I honestly felt like I had the flu.

On top of it all, Joyce had to drive home on Saturday, February 2, to check on her mother in the nursing home as well as other home business items. Just because I was going through this monumental medical situation, she still had to manage other things in our family and work. This is what I dealt with back in 1998 when Joyce was going through her breast cancer battle. Where I had to manage three children still at home, Joyce is an only child who had to manage her mother's situation. Fortunately, she lined up some close friends and neighbors who checked in on her mother and provided help while Joyce was in St. Louis. I was glad she was able to get away those days because I was sick from the preparation medications and did not want her to see me like this. The low-grade fevers gave way to constant vomiting and diarrhea, and I was beginning to understand more why

Dr. Wade wanted me to put on that extra body weight prior to the transplant. I was in the bathroom almost constantly for several days.

Days -3 and -2 had the chemo meds but not more ATG (yea!!). On Monday the 4th, I started receiving Tacrolimus, an anti-rejection drug to suppress my body's ability to reject the infused stem cells. Besides the immediate negative side effects that I had to deal with and since I would be taking this med for a long time, I also had to watch for longer term issues. The nurses were telling me that at this point, mouth sores and continued digestive issues were common problems that most transplant patients had to deal with for a while.

Day -1 had Rituxan chemo that took over three hours to receive and with all the negative effects of these preparation meds over the last six days, those 15 extra pounds that I put on over the last several months were being chipped away. I had no appetite at all and could only eat small amounts of food. The nurses pushed fluids at me, and I did what I could to drink enough to stay somewhat hydrated.

Joyce came back from her trip home late that Monday afternoon and stayed at a local hotel again. I encouraged her to stay at a hotel, so she could get a decent night's sleep with her neck problems which would be exacerbated by a fold-out bed. Unfortunately, her mother was not wanting to eat or drink much in the nursing home and even getting out of bed was a push. She was supposed to start physical therapy but often refused to cooperate. This difficult situation weighed on Joyce but was helped by our close friends and neighbors, who stepped in to visit Joyce's mother and to encourage her progress, as well as keeping Joyce informed of her status.

Our one bright spot was our 4-year old granddaughter, Ariya, who was always a great cheerleader for her papaw. Ariya had been born in 2008 with her intestines outside her body, and she spent a month in the newborn intensive care unit. That time seems like a very distant memory as we see how healthy and vibrant she now is – a God-sent reminder that this, too, shall pass. Although I could not have visitors, I could communicate with her and other people on the computer through Skype. As much as my family wanted to visit me, I told them that given my fragile state and the colds and flu that were so prominent at that time, that I just could not take the risk.

The fifth-floor medical staff encouraged all the patients on this floor receiving stem cell transplants to not just sit or lay in bed but get up and walk around as much as possible. They were concerned that pneumonia could set in. An exercise room across the hall from my hospital room contained a treadmill, elliptical and recumbent stationary bike. I tried to get in there every day and do something, because I had plenty of time in between the tests and getting drugs pumped into me. Especially during the week of prep, I felt so bad that I just could not exercise. The physical therapy people put a chart on each patient's door and gave a star on the chart for every day the patient was up and active. Here I was, a 52-year-old man feeling like a kindergartner back at elementary school trying to get stars on my paper. And being the over-achiever, I secretly wanted those stars!

Day 0, February 6, 2013 finally arrived with me having a zero white blood count, meaning no immune system was left after the Arm 2 preparation. I was ready for my donor's stem cells. The drugs did what Dr. Westervelt said they would—eradicate my remaining immune system which could fight off the new transplanted stem cells. Around 10:00 am, the equipment to accomplish this was brought to my room. It consisted of a chamber that looked like a roasting pan containing warm water sitting on top of a wheeled cart. Shortly thereafter, a tall metal cylinder, looking like an old-fashioned metal milk container, arrived; the vital frozen pack of stem cells was removed and quickly put in the warm water bath to thaw.

Offering comic relief, a gallon-sized zip lock bag of dum-dum suckers was pulled out of the bottom of the cart with all the tubes. I was offered my "favorite flavor" and grabbed a strawberry one. They told us that the infusion of stem cells causes a nasty taste in the mouth, and the dum-dums help negate that taste. They also told me that once the infusion began, my body would give off an aroma of "creamed corn." The first bag of pre-meds (strong sedatives and antihistamines) were now being pumped into me, like what I always had before each chemo infusion. I became extremely drowsy and was vaguely aware that more people were entering my room.

I realized this was not so humorous as this large team of people connected me to a heart monitor and watched me closely during the infusion of the stem cells. I was told that some people have severe reactions to the infusion that could include major organs ceasing to function. I also remembered that Dr. Wade telling me that once the stems cells are in my body there is no reversing the process. Whatever happens they cannot get them back out of my body. This reminded me of the difference between a pig and a chicken when making breakfast. The chicken participated but the pig was all in. Looks like I am providing the bacon for this one!

It took about 15 minutes to thaw the frozen donor's stem cells in the water bath. I expected them to be red like blood; however, white cells/stem cells are not red, so the pack was pinkish. The substance looked more a creamy tomato soup or a pound of fatty ground beef than the vibrant red I was expecting. A nurse hooked up the bag to my tri-fusion port for the infusion, but the process could not begin until a doctor arrived to oversee the actual infusion of stem cells.

Since this was the "Tide concentrate" variety, I only got one bag and it took all of 10 minutes to be infused into my body through the tri-fusion port. If this had not been pre-processed, multiple bags would have taken hours to do this infusion. By doing it this way, I received only the vital stem cells needed. The medical people continued to watch me to see if there were any adverse reactions to the infusion, but fortunately, I was boring to watch. Nothing negative happened other than me being nervous all day about what could happen.

I cannot recall all the medications that they gave me that day, but I felt very tired and slept off and on. Several medical people told me that most recipients of allogeneic stem cell transplants (also called bone marrow transplants since the stem cells eventually create and replace your bone marrow) develop various types of graft versus host issues which is the body trying to reject the transplanted stem cells. Since the new bone marrow and blood created by the donor's stem cells go throughout the whole body, and they are different than the original bone marrow and blood, the body's other organs try to fight off what they see as foreign substances.

The medical staff said that your skin is your body's largest organ and that is where they typically see the most problems. Therefore, there is so much testing in finding a suitable donor to try to minimize these rejection issues as much as possible. For my donor, the DNA tests matched ten out of ten markers and my donor even had the same blood type as me (A positive)! These measurements were positive factors in my favor for minimal graft versus host problems but only time would tell how much graft versus host would occur. I was also warned about the coming storm within my body from all the prep meds given the previous week. The nursing staff warned that killing off the immune system also leaves the digestive system wide open for unhealthy bacteria to multiply and cause profuse diarrhea.

Now I wait for those baby new stem cells to take root in my body and create the killer cells needed to fight off the leukemia that will try again to rear its ugly head. Unlike my old set of blood cells, which did not see the leukemia as a threat and would not fight it, these new cells will do the deed and kill the invader. The chromosomal deletion that prevented my immune system from attacking the leukemia should be present in my donor's DNA and will fight the cancer cells that might try and return. In the meantime, I must wait for all my blood counts to increase and for my body to stay free of fungal, bacterial, and viral infections. On this day I had NO immune system, and all precautions are being taken to assure that none of these gain a foothold.

Tomorrow the apartment will be available for Joyce to move everything to and give her a secure place to unwind on the days she is here. It will also be my home away from home once I was discharged from the hospital.

Chapter 7

Recovery at Barnes Hospital (Feb 2013 – Mar 2013)

Transplant is officially finished and now the waiting game begins. Waiting for those new stem cells to take root in my body, multiply, and create new bone marrow and blood. This will be the battle royale between the new stem cells and my old ones that had gotten knocked down from the ATG and other medications that I received the first seven days in the hospital.

The doctors told me that in future bone marrow biopsies, they would be able to tell what percentage of my bone marrow was from the new stem cells versus the old existing marrow. The process of changing over from the old me to the new me is called *chimerism*. I got a blood test every day that documented my red, white and platelet counts. The labs were drawn early in the morning, and then we played a waiting game until the nurse came in later to "post" the results on the white board on the wall. The Barnes medical personnel stated that patients typically need transfusions of both red blood cells and platelets, but they would only be administered if needed. The white blood cells would have to be created in my body by the new bone marrow from the infused stem cells.

Eventually, when my ANC count was high enough over several days (Absolute Neutrophil Count of >1,500), they would discharge me to a local apartment. The neutrophils are the part of the white blood cells that fight off bacteria and infection -- vital to my survival before going back into the "real world." My exit from the hospital was also dependent upon me staying free from fungal, bacterial, and viral infections while my entire immune system was rebuilding from zero. I was confined to staying on the fifth floor and avoiding any close contact with other people to protect myself from picking up something. I was told it would probably take three to four weeks for me to achieve this number.

On the first day after the transplant, I started with a different chemotherapy and immune system suppressant drug called Methotrexate. I really felt a little better and was able to get up and walk around the hallways on the fifth floor several times. We also attended a session in the family visiting room that reviewed "life after discharge." There was one poor lady in this session that had mouth sores so bad that she could not speak and could only barely open her mouth. Her caregiver told us the lining of her mouth was like raw hamburger. Just when you think what you have is so bad, you see someone else with something worse. That made me thankful to God for what I did have.

Unfortunately, my ankles and feet were swollen at the

end of this day probably because I overdid it. Apparently, all the walking and sitting up cause fluid to collect down there and I had to go back to the elevated feet in bed.

Last month before I was admitted, I had my send-off party, and everyone wore the *Team Larry* tee shirts. Joyce also made a stocking hat and hooded sweatshirt with *Larry V2.0.* Since my career has been in computers, I thought of myself with the new bone marrow and blood as a *new* version, much like new versions of software. This was a good way to bring some humor into my situation as the nurses and staff that came to my room were able to laugh with me while I sported the attire that kept me warm in the hospital.

Later that afternoon, Joyce moved into the two bedroom, fully furnished apartment that we had leased for my extended stay in the St. Louis area. It was just six miles west of the hospital and in a nice neighborhood near the Galleria. Now she had a better place to stay and would get this ready for me to move to when I was discharged. I was relieved that she could have a decent place to sleep at night and a safely gated garage to store the car but was still close enough to get to me in a moment's notice if need be.

Joyce received a call that day that her mother had contracted a clostridium difficile (*C. Diff)* infection that is highly contagious; consequently, she was moved to a private room at the nursing home. This condition was likely due to the high-powered antibiotics she had been taking to rid herself of the urinary tract infection. Her room, like mine, was at the end of a hallway in their building, and *C. Diff* was also something for which I was being monitored due to my lack of an immune system at this time. Fortunately, Joyce's *Mom Team* of helpers were there to assist her mother while Joyce was with me. It was ironic that both her mother and I were in isolation at the same time but in two different places.

My mother was still recovering from her stroke and had some residual issues with the vision in her right eye. Besides that, she was back to normal, which was a relief for me given all the issues Joyce's mother had. Mom reminded me several times that it was my fault she had the stroke, because she was so worried about me and my situation. Fortunately, my older brother and sister-in-law lived in the Springfield area and were able to take care of my mother's needs during this period.

I got more Methotrexate on Day +3 and Day +6 and another round of Rituxan on Day +7. I guess I thought my days getting chemo would be over once the transplant occurred, but these were given to ensure my body would receive the new cells properly and reject any cancer that might be in my system. Once my new bone marrow was functioning as it should, it would send the T-cells to take out any leukemia.

The medical staff kept telling me that I would start feeling worse again but so far that had not happened. Other than some headaches, which were probably from the chemo cocktail I was getting, I was not experiencing significant negative symptoms and was even starting to get a slight appetite back. I got a pad for my bed to make it a little more comfortable but was still not getting much sleep. In fact, I was amazed at how little sleep I was getting and still be able to somewhat function. With feeling so bad 24/7, having a rubber mattress on the hospital bed, and getting vitals checked continually, I only got about a total of an hour of sleep at night and then a nap during the day of about an hour. This caused some real challenges mentally and emotionally since I was in a sleep-deprived state all the time. I tried to stay positive, but it was hard given the environment on the fifth floor and how ill I felt most of the time. With little rest and the confinement on top of that, I was beginning to have some real problems with my attitude. One thing that really helped on Valentine's Day (one-week post-transplant) was a photo my stepson Justin in Los Angeles snapped while waiting at a stop light. The car in front of him had a banner across the back hatch that said *GO TEAM LARRY!* Now what are the odds of him seeing a car in LA with that across the back? It is amazing how our Father in heaven can let you know that he is watching over you. This was also the first day my ANC finally came up from 0 to 30. It was a small step but at least it was a start.

Another source of encouragement was the relationships I was developing with other transplant patients on my floor. As we walked the hallways of the fifth floor, we got to know our medical support staff better as well as some of our fellow patients and their family members. Two guys I got to know well were Ken and Pat. Ken was a policeman from Peoria, Illinois, and Pat was an attorney from Belleville,

Illinois. Their wives were up here also, so Joyce and I got to talk with them and learn their stories. It was nice to have some comradery with these folks and help encourage each other since we all were dealing with similar struggles.

On February 16, 2013 (Day +10), my daughter-in-law Elizabeth, Justin's wife, came in from LA to help Joyce. This was a huge benefit to both of us. Having Elizabeth here to assist in my needs and free up Joyce to be able to go back home and handle work items and take care of her 95-year-old mother's situation in the nursing home was invaluable right now.

Joyce's mom was not progressing at all and still had the catheter bag, was unable to walk without assistance, or even pull herself up out of a chair. This formerly active senior was also beginning to deal with some depression over her current situation, and it was vital that Joyce could commute back and forth to tend to her needs as well.

Joyce flew back to Decatur from St. Louis on 02/19/13 to take care of home, work, and her mother. This allowed Elizabeth to use our Toyota Camry to drive back and forth from the apartment to the hospital and watch over me. Joyce then drove our Dodge Journey which had been in the garage at home this whole time back to St. Louis on February 23rd, so both of our vehicles would be at our disposal.

I got Methotrexate on Day +11 and Rituxan on Day +14 and did not have any significant negative side effects; however, the Cytoxan chemo at the beginning of the month caused me to lose all my hair except my eyebrows. Different types of chemo have different side effects, and everything I received before now did not cause hair loss. Truthfully, I had already given up the hair on my head a few years ago since it was thinning on top with a hairline heading farther north at a rapid pace (no comb-over here). I had a mustache for most of the last 40 years and being without it seemed strange. Loss of this brought a major change to my appearance. I was uncomfortable about this until my daughter-in-law told me that I looked like present-day Bruce Willis after losing the mustache. That sold it for me. No more facial hair! Some of the nurses thought it might be a big deal for me and cut out a paper moustache for me to wear if I felt I needed it. Just these small attempts at humor made all the difference in my moods, because the days were starting to get long and the confinement increasingly bothersome.

My all-important ANC started going up some but then would retreat. It went up to 177, then 196, up to 460, but then down to 330, then back to 406 on 02/20/13. I was feeling better by this time and getting a more normal appetite back. I asked about getting an exercise mat in my room, and the nurse told me that they had what they called "fall mats" to place by patients' beds to protect them in case they fell out of bed.

Well, I got one but not for falling. I had taught early morning aerobics for 10 years and had a routine of floor stretches and exercises that I now wanted to start doing every day. I was sure to clean my *fall mat* with disinfecting wipes before I used it every day. My morning routine now was getting out of bed around 7-7:30am, walking the floor for a warmup, and then going to the workout room across the hall from my room and doing a 20-minute bike ride. After this, I would order breakfast (which took about a half hour to arrive) and then get on my *fall mat* to do my floor routine. I had a star on my door for every day I had been there, and I wanted to keep the streak going. When this was completed, my breakfast would arrive, and I would eat, get my shower, and get dressed for the day. Because the extensions on the Hickman tri-port hung outside my body, the nurses showed me how to tape cling wrap in a square over the entire Hickman to keep it dry while I showered.

My wife and daughter-in-law would arrive in the morning and would stay until late afternoon. Sometimes they would bring reheat able meals and join me for dinner, and other times they left to have dinner together at the apartment. I did not feel it necessary for them to stay with me all day and all evening, and I passed the time by reading and listening to music. My sleep was still very broken, and I often dozed off in the evening times with the room free of other people.

When Joyce and Elizabeth were with me, we would walk around and talk with staff and other patients and their care givers. All 31 rooms on the floor were occupied every day. When someone was discharged, or when a patient died (which was a regular occurrence on this floor), all furnishings were moved out of the room and it was completely cleaned and disinfected before the next patient was admitted. One of the most difficult parts of my daily walk was seeing a bed in the hallway early in the day and the cleaning staff in the room. That usually meant the patient died because the planned discharges were always later in the day. The clean-up began as soon as the person left the room, and the next transplant candidate arrived to take the available space as each person had their own private room. The room with the lady that had the terrible mouth sores was one of those that was vacated early one day. As I strolled those halls, I prayed for the souls in each one of the rooms.

Almost every Saturday evening, one of the male nurses would bring his guitar and sing songs in the family visitation room for anyone who could make it there. He was truly kind, and we talked a lot about our mutual love for music. He and his wife both worked on this floor, and I was amazed at how special people had to be to deal with 31 patients going through stem cell transplants. My relationships with the nursing staff were interesting. The facility automatically rotated my personal nurses every few days. This was done to keep the staff from getting too attached to the patients and vice-versa. Even still, occasionally I would have the same person pop up again, and it was always pleasant when it was one of the staff who was really on top of things. Just as in any profession, there were some nurses who were better than others in terms of sheer ability to do the medical testing and being a comfort to me through their conversation.

The facility had a complaint system in place to report a staff member who had done something wrong. In my entire stay there, I did not think I would need to use the option, but one nurse, Donna, really triggered it. When she arrived one morning to clean my port (this had to be done manually every day to prevent infection) she began pulling on the extensions like I was a cow to be milked! I honestly thought she might yank the whole thing out of my chest, and I could see the skin under the port excessively pulling forward towards her. Joyce was in the room and noticed this gal was being rather rough with me and hastily doing the blood extractions too. I told her to please "take it easy there," but she stated she had been in nursing almost 30 years and knew what she was doing. After she left the room, Joyce said she would contact the supervisor and inform them of what had occurred. I never saw Donna again.

By February 25, my ANC was up to 854 but the next day dropped to 640. This was nowhere near the goal of 1500. My entire team was starting to get discouraged because it would be four weeks on 02/27/13 since I was admitted, and I had been told by several staff personnel that I should be preparing for discharge. I know they meant well, but my expectations were getting set for a faster recovery than what was happening. Although I had my daily routine and was able to use my laptop computer for music, reading and sometimes interacting with other people, I was still confined to the fifth floor and it was beginning to feel like incarceration.

Talking with Ken, my fellow patient and now new friend, he too was having a roller coaster but his was his platelet count. He had to have several transfusions, and the effect was only minimal before the counts would bottom out again. We both agreed that the staff was trying to be helpful and encouraging, but their over-optimistic view that our counts would increase soon just caused us frustration. We shared this with the hospital staff to please temper their positive predictions to help us keep realistic perspectives on our timeline for eventual release. By now the frustration began to turn darker with more negative feelings. I was blessed by this time not to have needed ANY transfusions of either red or platelet cells. The staff had pretty much assured me that every patient will need these after the transplant, but God covered me on that aspect, and while my counts were not within normal ranges, they were acceptable enough to prevent the need for a transfusion. But still the darkness enveloped me.

With so much idle time, I would often sit and look out the fifth-floor windows and watch people and vehicles moving up and down the street below wondering about the hectic pace of all our lives and how we pushed so hard to get things done. I was thankful also that I was on the north side of the building and could look out and see this. The rooms on the other side of the floor looked upon another brick wall of the hospital. But having all this *free* time only made me realize how helpless I felt. My poor wife was meeting herself coming and going trying to manage her mom's care, our business, and taking care of me. I had always been there to be a contributing part of our marriage and business, and now all I could do is stare out a window. I felt useless and helpless.

I reflected on my almost 53 years and how my life also had been filled with busy schedules and to-do lists. My current schedule consisted of extraordinarily little *to-do* and just hoping that my blood counts would increase so I could get back to my lifestyle prior to the cancer invasion. The nagging thought was "would that happen?" At that time, I was feeling somewhat better and not seeing any major problems, but what if I developed long term debilitating issues and ended up with a lower quality of life? Given the long list of possible chronic problems that allogeneic stem cell transplants can cause, this was a real possibility that concerned me. What would my life be like from now on and when would I ever get out of this hospital? Would my white blood count ever get up to a healthy level or would I have to live a "boy in the bubble" life with a constant fear of catching some disease that would do serious damage to me? The medical people were very adamant about this ANC being the key indicator of how strong my immune system was and without enough of these white blood cells, a multitude of common illnesses could be serious if not fatal to me. As I struggled with these questions along with the lack of getting a good night's sleep, I was finding myself emotionally sliding down into more negative feelings about the confinement in this hospital. I was never an anxiety-prone person, but with each day that went by, I became more and more consumed with the thought that this may be my existence for the future.

I also regularly stared at different building structures that were north of the hospital. I really liked looking at the St. Nicholas Greek Orthodox Church that was right across the street. The stained-glass windows were very colorful and pretty to look at and a reminder that God was ever-present.

To some, this would have had no meaning, but this view, and the cross atop that building, was one of hope to me and one of the few tangible things I had to grasp onto. This also was the one of my favorite places to reflect on my Christian faith and try to communicate with God because I was so limited as to where I could go. As the end of February 2013 approached, fear and frustration were turning into depression; I struggled to find strength to combat it. The mental, social, and physical activities that I had been doing were not addressing this emotional downward slide, and I really had no way to deal with this.

Seeing the other patients on this floor suffering so severely from cancer also caused me to question God about his love and goodness. As I prayed with more desperation, I could not sense anything from the Holy Spirit. I had also talked with my wife and my closest Christian friend, Bob, about this and asked them if God had communicated with them spiritually in any way. Bob, Joyce, and I had all experienced the Holy Spirit at certain times in our pasts individually as well as together. During Joyce's cancer battle, we all had sensed the presence of Christ through the Spirit on multiple occasions and His peace and miraculous pain relief for Joyce which had occurred. He gave her guidance to make key decisions about using her situation to help others dealing with breast cancer after her recovery. But now we all felt like we were in a spiritual desert with no word or touch from our Lord and Savior Jesus. At times it truly felt like a desert of isolation, and although I was blessed to not have the horrible things that were predicted like the constant diarrhea, mouth sores, infections, and transfusions, I still found myself getting further and further into a *black hole*. I did not want to burden Joyce, and at times kept many of these dark feelings to myself.

On Sunday, March 3, 2013, the head oncology doctor at Barnes Hospital saw me in the morning and told me that I was going to get to go to the apartment the next day. My ANC had gotten up to 1045 on March 1 but then fell again the next day to 943. Despite this, I still had not experienced any of the possible serious physical problems that typically happen with allogeneic stem cell transplant patients. I did however start developing a skin rash, but the staff gave me a steroid cream to alleviate the itching for now and they were not overly concerned. This doctor told me that he was reviewing my case on all aspects, not just the ANC white blood count. Tears of joy and relief flowed down my face and Joyce's. Finally, FINALLY, I would get out of here and get to be with my wife and daughter-in-law at the apartment on Monday. Could this cloud over me finally be moving on?

All my elation happened prior to my daily blood test and when the results came back later that day, my ANC had plummeted to around 600. I found it hard to believe it could have dropped that much when it was supposed to be rising daily and asked them to please repeat the test. By Monday morning it was *below* 600. When another doctor who was covering the fifth floor saw me on Monday morning, he decided that I was not going anywhere, yet. That broke me emotionally. After the doctor left the room, I asked Joyce to please leave because I was about to lose it. She did not want to go, but I kissed her and told her very emphatically that I needed some time alone to deal with this. After she left, I lost all emotional control and began shouting and crying. Never in my life did I have such an outburst. I got on my knees and beat my fists and arms on the hospital bed as hard and long as I could. The tension that had been building finally was released, but I was in even a more foreboding state than I had been previously.

After physically exhausting myself, I put on a hooded sweatshirt and pulled the hood up over my head. Feeling totally defeated and despondent, I shuffled around the hallways by myself with my head down that whole day. I went to the window in the family visitation room and again stared out at the Greek Orthodox church feeling so alone, frightened, and isolated. I was in a darkness that is hard to describe, and I just wanted to give up. For the first time in this long cancer battle, my emotions really overwhelmed me with negative and depressive thoughts and feelings. I even despaired of the thought of continuing to live. I thought, "What's the use? I will never be free from this medical prison even if I am discharged." The isolation had taken its toll, and I was in a hole I could not climb out of. I retreated to my room and wondered when or if I would ever leave this place. It truly had become my prison.

Apparently, I was not the first patient to "lose it." I had forgotten that there was a small camera eye on the ceiling above me, and the hospital staff was watching me on a monitor the entire time I was having the outburst in my room. Prior to this I had been their "low-maintenance" patient and the "poster kid" for transplants (not my words—

just things the nurses and staff told me while I was there). Those shiny stars reflecting my daily activity progress on my door meant nothing to me right then because I felt so defeated. A short time after I returned to my room a chaplain was sent in to talk with me. I did not request one, but the staff obviously saw that I needed help. She was kind and considerate of my struggles and tried to help me to see that I was not as alone as I was feeling.

Unbeknownst to me, Joyce had driven back to Mount Zion Monday evening and had called our close Christian friend, Bob, to tell him what happened and how I was in desperate need of intercessory prayer. She tearfully told him how I had lost all strength and will to keep going. She told me later she had never seen me like this in our entire married life and she was afraid for me. She confided that she was so fearful that she was going to lose both her husband and her mom, and like me, felt helpless. Elizabeth stayed behind in St. Louis, but I did not want any visitors. Truthfully, I just wanted to die.

Later that night I was again sitting by the window looking out at that church when a strange thought came to me. "Larry doesn't have cancer" was rolling around inside my head. I said to myself, "Now that is the stupidest thing I have ever thought! Well, if I don't have cancer, what am I doing here?" Then the next thought came in with, "Larry doesn't have cancer; his *human body* has cancer. Larry can't get cancer." Immediately, I saw in my head my 2010 Dodge Journey vehicle and the internal conversation continued with a comparison of my human body and my vehicle. I began thinking about the similarities between the two. I walk around in one and I drive the other, I spend a lot of time and money keeping them running well, and even with great preventive maintenance, someday the Dodge Journey will eventually wear out and not be worth repairing when it develops a serious mechanical or electrical problem.

My human body will also stop working someday when it wears out due to age and/or succumbs to a physical failure due to disease or an accident. Then another question came in my brain, "What do you do when your Dodge Journey is no longer worth repairing?" I thought, "Well, I go buy a new vehicle." And the next thought really enlightened me: "Right, and when your human body wears out, you will get a new body."

Being a Christian for almost 30 years, I always compare my thoughts and ideas with the truth found in the Bible to make sure I am not just operating in my own knowledge. I know my ideas and thinking can be wrong, but I have found over these years that when I line up with God's Word, I am guaranteed to be right. Reviewing God's Word regarding what happens after the human body dies, I found that this perspective completely lined up with the Word. Specifically, 1 Corinthians 15 describes the differences between the earthly body and resurrected body. As I pondered all of this on that Monday evening, I concluded that I never had and can never get cancer. My *human body* has cancer and someday will die, but when that happens, I will move from this earthly body to my new resurrected body, just like I will someday replace my vehicle. My soul, the eternal part of me and the *real Larry*, cannot be impacted by cancer or transplants or anything dire that may happen to my physical body and that is the Larry that God was speaking to me about.

While processing all of this, I noticed the darkness and depression dissipating. I thanked God for speaking to my heart and mind and allowing me to have a breakthrough. This was not just some positive thinking, because I was doing that and not getting out from under the negative emotions. I realized that my Father had waited until I had given up before stepping in to give me the lifeline that I needed. Just like a lifeguard waiting for the drowning person to give up before saving him, God waited until I had emotionally been broken to the point of completely giving up to impart His Word. What I had known in my mind was finally transferred to my heart. While I always knew cancer was more than just a physical battle, I was now being taught a very deep truth about my own frailty and my need to not just know God's Word, but to give up my own plans and desires to totally surrender my life to Him. Jesus said it this way in Matthew 16:25, "For whoever would save his life will lose it, but whoever loses his life for my sake will find it." Funny how the application of that is so much easier to read than to actually live out.

Like I said before, I had experienced multiple times of God speaking to my heart and giving me direction to make decisions in my life. Like any relationship, it takes time and effort to get to know someone else and learn how to communicate with them in a deeper way. But this situation was much more intense and painful than anything I had ever experienced. I do not want to give the impression that everything was great after this encounter. I was still in the hospital and my ANC white blood count was still too low to allow me to leave. But the difference was that I decided to *accept* my situation and just trust Him. Even if my physical body would never be like it was, I was not going to focus on this three-dimensional world but to look beyond it to the One who created everything, including me. I also focused on the fact that all this pain and suffering that I was enduring was temporary and it would end sooner or later (I just did not know which that would be). I felt confident going forward that no matter what, God had me covered.

The next morning, I called my wife and told her what had happened the previous night. It is hard to explain, really, but it was far more than anything I could have mustered up on my own. I wanted deliverance from my situation, and now asked for God's peace and solace to accept my situation. Although I wanted out of the hospital as badly as ever, I now had a new calm about it and truly accepted the unknown future. Whether it was two days or two more weeks, I was at peace with my situation.

And just as I had relinquished all this, by Wednesday, March 6, my ANC jumped to over 1800. Thursday it dropped back to 1300 but I kept believing. The doctors finally agreed that there was no higher risk of going to the apartment by waiting a couple of more days, so I was released to go to our St. Louis apartment that day!

I wish I could say that leaving the floor was bittersweet, but other than leaving behind the wonderful staff, I never wanted to see a hospital room again. As was always the case, the paperwork delayed my being able to leave until mid-afternoon. The minutes ticked by slowly, but by 4pm, I was breathing air that was not scrubbed clean, stepping on actual pavement, and physically walking on my own in the apartment and looking forward to sleeping in a real bed! I finally had freedom after over a month in the hospital. And just when I thought my journey was ending, I found it was just taking a new turn.

Look Up

Chapter 8

Recovery in St. Louis Apartment (Mar 2013 – Apr 2013)

Getting out of the fifth floor was amazingly refreshing. Although having to wear the N95 mask for protection against airborne illnesses, I was able to take it off once I got into the apartment. Joyce did a wonderful job getting a two bedroom-two full bathroom, completely furnished apartment about six miles west of Barnes hospital. She also surprised me with bringing my digital piano and amp from home! Knowing how music was a key part of my emotional health, she had our neighbor help her pack it and get it in the vehicle so I could enjoy playing my piano in the St. Louis apartment.

The Villas at Brentwood is a large complex whose gated parking garage backs up into a large shopping plaza which contained Target, Bed Bath and Beyond, and Trader Joe's. Across the street was a Whole Foods, a Michael's craft store, and several other nice places. Within walking distance were two sizeable parks and plenty of places to eat. Our unit was on the fourth floor and had a small balcony that looked out towards the park area. It had high 10' ceilings and was about 1200 square feet in size. A small gym area was available on the ground floor. To enter the covered garage area, a code had to be given to allow the gate to open. Having a covered garage was another thing that was especially nice during the late winter months. Many of the places that were nearer to the hospital only offered street parking, and some of the streets did not look too safe.

Arriving at the apartment was another huge step in my recovery process. It had been thirty days since my stem cell transplant, and the thought of a real bed and real food was so appealing to me! Even though I was now in a normal bed, I was not able to sleep well due to the 37 in-patient days of next to no sleep every single day. I was sleep deprived for sure, but that new memory foam bed sure felt good. At that time Joyce was still in Mount Zion and would not get back until Saturday. She left Elizabeth and I a tasty set of easy to prepare meals which were a welcome change from the hospital fare. The food on the fifth floor was not bad, but it was not what I was accustomed to and was rather bland.

The next day I was hungry for my favorite lunch food, Subway. Elizabeth, my daughter- in-law, and I walked over to a nearby Subway to eat lunch. That fresh crisp early March air smelled so good even through a N95 mask. It was in the low 50's temperature-wise, and the beckon of spring was in the air. We sat at a table that was as far away as possible from other people to protect me, but we went at a good time in the mid- afternoon since it was after the lunch hour. Boy, that sandwich sure tasted great and the ability to walk around outside was fantastic!

Joyce got there on Saturday and I was so happy to see her at the apartment instead of at the hospital. The last time we were together was such a difficult situation with my emotional meltdown due to the inability to check out when scheduled.

To celebrate, my mom, brother, and sister-in-law came for a visit on Sunday afternoon from Springfield, IL. It was great to see them, but I had begun to develop a slight rash and I could tell I had a slight fever. I had the low-grade fevers frequently while in the hospital and the area of the rash was so small, I initially was not concerned. I was so happy to finally see some close family, and I know they were equally happy to see me alive and doing well. I did not want to mention initially that I had developed this rash, because I was certain it was nothing and would go away quickly. We ordered some wood-fired pizzas from a local place for dinner and were all in a triumphant mood. As tasty as the pizza was, I had no appetite and knew I was getting worse. We contacted our Barnes oncologist's office, and they recommended the steroid cream for the itchy skin. Now I was concerned about getting sick and having to go back to the hospital. I had only been out a few days.

By Tuesday, March 12, the rash worsened, and the fever got higher. We already had a bone marrow biopsy, lab work and follow-up appointment scheduled with the Barnes nurse practitioner that day so after going through all of that, the doctor was called in and one of my worst fears materialized. I was re-admitted to the fifth floor at 6pm. This time was put in room 5914 instead of 5925 and had a view of the wall of the building next to mine rather than the scenic view of the little church. Oh well, at least it was a different view, and I was hoping I would only be there a brief time.

Even though I was not feeling well, I played some piano in the lobby area wearing my N95 mask prior to my testing and re-admission. Music continued to help me cope with the pain and uncertainty, and this day, unfortunately, was plagued with that uncertainty. Going back onto the fifth floor was obviously difficult and those feelings of fear and depression were coming upon me again. Was this going to be my new life? Would my new immune system ever allow me to get out of a controlled environment? Would I ever feel well again?

I kept reminding myself of my experience earlier this month, where the One who made me and made this physical body provided His strength and peace to me regardless of these conditions. No matter the medical outcome, I was not allowing the physical circumstances to dictate my attitude. This time I was able to deal with this in a new way by resting in His power, provision, and perspective.

During this hospital stay, a whole gamut of testing was performed on me to try and determine the cause of these issues. Was it due to my body trying to reject the new bone marrow or something else? Now, nearly my entire body was covered in a bright red, itchy rash. A skin biopsy was also performed and even after all the testing, nothing conclusive was found. Was this the dreaded graft-vs-host beginning to manifest, or an allergy to the medicines I was on?? Some of the results pointed to an allergic reaction, but the remedy was the same—high doses of prednisone and steroid cream. A large tub of this cream (think of a Country Crock butter tub) arrived in my room and I was slathered from head to toe with this stuff; the rash slowly began to retreat.

I remembered other patients released and readmitted during my initial 37 days in the hospital, so this situation did not come as a total surprise. I was also given a new round of antibiotics, and the fever, too, subsided.

During all of this, our home church choir had purchased "Team Larry" t-shirts from us to help fund-raise for my medical bills. Upon hearing of my readmission, they sent me a video of the choir cheering "Go Team Larry!!" wearing their shirts. They will never know the extent of what a huge blessing and inspiration it was for me to see all my friends from church letting me know that they were praying for my recovery! Apparently, God was listening to them, too! After six long days, and the fortieth day after my bone marrow transplant, I was back in the apartment taking all these additional medications hoping I could stay out of the hospital. The rapid onset made me realized just how fragile my new immune system was.

While all of this was happening, Joyce had some decisions to make about the assisted living apartment her mother resided at prior to her fall. The cost of the apartment was $3300 a month, and from the prognosis the doctors were giving, her mom would unlikely be able to return because she had the catheter bag and was still not able to rise from a chair on her own. The C-Diff infection from earlier in the month weakened her further, and from everything the doctors said, she would most likely have to stay in the skilled nursing home the rest of her life. She paid for the month of February because Pauline was admitted to the nursing home the day before we left for St. Louis and we were hopeful she would recover and be able to return there. It was now nearing the end of March, and her mom's apartment needed to be vacated.

Joyce and Elizabeth both headed to Mt. Zion that week to move the remaining items in the apartment to our house and close out the lease there. The personal belongings (clothing, dishes, wall décor, linens, etc.) also had to be packed up and moved out.

Joyce phoned when they first arrived there and told me the refrigerator was making a loud, funny noise. I directed her to the file that contained the warranty and purchase info, and we discovered our refrigerator was 19 years old. This was not a time to go appliance shopping, but we decided there was no alternative. Our refrigerator was making a sound indicating a bearing was going out, and the repairs would exceed the value. Joyce and Elizabeth were tasked with this, and Joyce found a perfect fridge in the right color and size at our local Sears. Unfortunately, Sears would not be able to deliver it till the following week. By then, the girls would be back in St. Louis, and there was no guarantee the current one would hold out that long.

Joyce called our plumber friend Larry, and he said he would pick the fridge up and bring it by the next evening and install the ice maker as well. Getting the new one over the railing of the house, through the doors, and up the steps into the kitchen proved daunting. Larry the Plumber, (as we call him) and his father thought they would be able to manage it, but two neighbors of ours were enlisted when it just wasn't possible to get it in the door in a conventional fashion. Something that should have taken less than hour turned into a nearly three-hour ordeal before the new unit was up and running. Once again, a feeling of helplessness overcame me because I felt I should have been there to assist with all this.

The next day the girls resumed packing, and our good friends and neighbors were there to help on Saturday morning, March 23rd, to do the heavy lifting. This was the only opportunity for Joyce to get help since these people worked during the week. Those who had trucks and muscles moved the larger items like the bedroom and dining room furniture. It was another beautiful spring-like day. The next day a weather bombshell hit. That afternoon a major snowstorm rolled in and dropped 18 inches of snow in the Mount Zion area and a foot in St. Louis!

During that time that Joyce and Elizabeth were gone, my older brother came to be my caregiver for the first three days, then my mother came down and was with me for the next six days. They took me to my medical appointments and provided me with whatever I needed. Having my brother and mother be caregivers helped them see how I was really doing. I wanted them to know that I was mentally and emotionally doing well despite the physical issues.

On March 26, wc got the test results from the March 12 bone marrow biopsy. No leukemia was shown in the biopsy and 55% of my bone marrow was now from my donor. The blood tests from March 22 showed my platelets in normal range and red and white cells just below normal range. Although the process of my donor engraftment was a little slower than the doctor liked to see, my blood counts were steadily increasing, and I had no cancer, no fever, no rash and less fatigue. All aspects of my physical condition were trending in the right direction. My doctor cut the prednisone dose which provided me relief from the body shakes the drug caused, and I had no water gain from taking these steroids.

The apartment complex had that small workout room with some machines and free weights. During the mid-morning, I would go down there and perform a light workout each day. With the increase in physical activity, my appetite began to slowly increase. I also began to sleep a little more and more restfully. In the hospital, I could only get about an hour of sleep at night and about an hour during the day. I was amazed how I could still function, and my body could heal on that small amount of sleep. Now I was getting a few hours during the night and tried not to sleep at all during the day, but that was hard since I did not have much to do.

Joyce and Elizabeth got back to the apartment on

Wednesday, March 27, and my mother was able to go back home. I was getting my lab work and checkups several times each week because my oncologist was keeping a close watch on my condition. However, I was really feeling better, getting more energy, increasing my food intake, and my blood counts were holding steady.

On Saturday, March 30, we said goodbye to our daughter-in-law Elizabeth as she wanted to see her family in Missouri for Easter before she flew back to California. She was a huge help for us during her stay here, and we developed a close friendship through this time. We drove her to a mid-point in the state where her family met her. One of my first cousins and his family did not live far from there, and we planned to meet them for lunch before our trek back to St. Louis. Although the huge snowstorm was difficult for all of us, it was the end of the winter weather. Although Joyce and I had been through our own personal winter storms, we believed this springtime was coming with the promise of more healing underway.

With Elizabeth gone, we no longer needed two vehicles in St. Louis. Joyce drove the Camry back home on Thursday, April 4, and after I got lab work done on Friday morning, April 5, I drove our Dodge Journey back home to Mt. Zion that afternoon. Although the medical personnel wanted me to stay in St. Louis for the first 100 days, I was feeling well enough at this point to get a weekend stay back home. We stayed in our Mount Zion home until we drove together back to St, Louis on the evening of April 8. Sleeping for a couple of nights in my own bed at home was amazingly therapeutic. These few days being back in our home really helped my mental and emotional health as well as gave us time to get work and family tasks completed. I longed for the day when I could be back at home for good.

Tuesday, April 9, we went to Barnes Hospital for lab work and checkup. My white blood count dropped from 4.3 to 1.7, which technically made me neutropenic and very susceptible to getting sick. Having low white blood counts had been an issue ever since the transplant, but even with a lot of flu and other communicable diseases floating around, Joyce and I were able to avoid getting sick from them.

With this drop in my white blood count, another Barnes lab was performed on April 12, and my next bone marrow biopsy was moved up to April 17. In between these tests, we were able to come back to Mt. Zion, but I kept myself from being around other people to keep myself isolated for protection. The Barnes medical personnel told us that at around Day 60 this is a common occurrence for transplant patients, because they believe that the new donor cells and original bone marrow were battling for ultimate control. They called this becoming fully engrafted with my donor's cells which were now creating my bone marrow.

As we drove back to St. Louis the evening of April 16, we had dinner with some friends who live just west of St. Louis. As we were talking about our situation, they offered to allow us to stay at their condo to provide us an option rather than paying for the apartment. This was a wonderful offer that helped us decide to get out of the apartment at the end of April and stay at their condo if need be after that. I was feeling so much better and stronger and did not want to spend the entire month of May in St. Louis. These frequent trips back home during the month of April seemed to be issue free from my health perspective, and mentally, I needed the solace that my own home provided.

I got another bone marrow biopsy the next day, Wednesday April 17. I was now at day 70 from the transplant and had labs as well as an appointment with our Barnes nurse practitioner. I was supposed to get a CT Scan, but they forgot about my pre-meds to deal with the contrast dye allergy I have. Barnes scheduled the CT Scan to be done in Decatur on the next day at my local oncologist's practice since we were driving back home on Wednesday night.

Friday morning, I got a call from my oncologist, not one of his staff, and he told me to get to the local hospital immediately to receive an ultrasound doppler test for other areas of my body. The CT scan showed a small blood clot in my left lung area. As we were heading out the door, Barnes called with the results from the Wednesday labs and bone marrow biopsy – still no leukemia and my white blood count was up to 2.0. Although the white blood count was nowhere near what we would like to see, it was better than the previous test and a relief to hear some good news. The chimerism (percentage of my bone marrow now from my donor) results would be the following week.

We arrived at the hospital and the doppler test was performed on my neck, arms and legs (areas that the CT scan did not cover). Another blood clot was found in the jugular vein on the right side of my neck. Dr. Wade said that these were apparently due to the hardware in my body from the two ports. The one in my neck had been there a while because it was attached to the vein wall and was starting to be reabsorbed. Although I did not need to be hospitalized for these clots, I had to start taking blood thinning drugs every day to deal with these. This would have to be done for 3-6 months until the clots were completely gone.

By April 23, which was the day after my 53rd birthday, we were back in St. Louis to see my Barnes oncologist Dr. Westervelt for labs and a checkup. We were thrilled when he broke the news that the donor cells have won! The last bone marrow biopsy showed over 95% engrafted which also means that my blood counts are donor-created new cells. Now whatever my blood counts are, we know they are all new cells that will keep the leukemia gone! I had to return to Dr. Wade two days later to see how the blood thinners were working, but overall, things were looking up and I did not have to return to St. Louis again for two weeks.

After the appointment we moved the final items out of the St. Louis apartment and had a lovely Italian meal at Maggiano's before driving home that evening. Each time we came back to Mt. Zion that month, we brought a few items with us to lessen the load when we finally left. Now that day was here, and the last load was safely in our vehicle. Fortunately, we got everything out before a huge deluge of rain hit the area. It was a wet drive home, but the joy of going there overtook us both and the wet pavement and clouds seemed to lead the way.

Eliminating the month to month apartment cost was a huge financial relief for us. I prayed there will be no more overnight stays in St. Louis even though I was still dealing with fatigue, rashes, dry skin, low grade fevers, low blood counts, and blood clots. Normally a list of health issues that long would be overwhelming, but as I was learning, nothing in this process came quickly. For now, another chapter in this process was coming to an end.

Look Up

Chapter 9

Transplant Recovery at Home
(Apr 2013 – Dec 2013)

During the last few weeks in St. Louis, I purchased an android tablet because I saw several fellow musicians from church use tablets to store and view their sheet music. Now that I was living back at home and unable to get out much due to my degraded immune system from the low blood counts, I had a lot of time without much to do.

Having played piano for 45 years, I accumulated several large containers full of sheet music in various books and individual scores. As a recovery project, I started to scan sheet music into my computer and edited these songs to get them to fit and be visible on my tablet. This was a large undertaking since I had hundreds of songs to scan. I took each precious sheet of music, scanned it into the computer, then cropped the document or brightened the image to look its best on my new tablet. I loved how I could easily create folders by artist, song, or genre and I knew this would really help me when I played piano more down the road. I found it was easier to read on the tablet, too. This was a good project for me to do at home along with working with Joyce on garment orders. Loving music as I do, it was a positive distraction from the medical issues that continued.

A battery of tests (blood lab work, chest x-ray, IV antibiotics, and CT scans of my sinuses and chest) were scheduled for me at my local Decatur oncologist's practice on Friday, April 26. My constant low-grade fever was up to around 100 and body aches were getting worse. It was mid-afternoon, and Dr. Wade told us that this could be caused by something viral or there could be an infection in some of the hardware in my body. Reluctantly, I was admitted to a local hospital on that day (Day 80 from the transplant) for the weekend to check the lines in both ports and administer more IV antibiotics. With my white blood count being less than 2.0, these steps were necessary to get me the resources that I needed to keep this from becoming something much more serious. Going back into a hospital room was difficult to deal with even though this was supposed to be a short-term stay, but we trusted Dr. Wade's judgment and did not want to take any chances. No visitors were allowed due to my susceptibility to picking up infections which took me back to the struggle I had being isolated in St. Louis. I ran these low-grade temps almost daily, and while they became more of nuisance than anything, I agreed that it was time to get to the bottom of what was causing them.

I was discharged on Monday, April 29 (Thank God!) and all the cultures and tests came back negative, again. On Wednesday, May 1, we saw Dr. Wade and got more blood work completed. After reviewing all this information and still dealing with the fevers and aches, I got his approval to remove the Hickman tri-port catheter that had been placed by Barnes for the transplant. Dr Wade said he suspected there was some bacteria deep in the hardware that was facilitating the continuing fevers. The Barnes medical staff did not want me to get this out yet, but Joyce and I were convinced that even though the tests did not show any infection in the catheter, that was the probable cause of these issues. Yet another trip to the hospital, but this one was to remove some of my hardware. How differently I felt than when these objects were first inserted.

On May 3, at 7:00AM, I was at the local hospital interventional radiology department receiving local anesthetic on the left side of my chest. As the doctor was excising this hardware from inside my chest and neck, parts of it were proving difficult to remove. My skin had grown around parts of the tubes and connectors. Although I had gotten numbed in those areas, I could feel the pulling and tugging as the doctor struggled to get these items out of my body. Unlike my reaction to getting the first Power Port placed, by this point I just laid there and joked with the medical folks about getting filleted. After what seemed like an eternity, the doctor finally got all the hardware out and I was sore for quite a while afterward.

I experienced a new-found freedom in getting all that out of me and not having three tubes hanging out of my chest. No more putting saran wrap over the tri-port catheter when I took showers. Leaving the bionic parts that were hanging out of my chest behind again reinforced the feelings that things were getting back to normal. And as we suspected, immediately after this procedure, the fevers were completely gone! Joyce and I were right that even though the blood tests did not show any infections, this catheter was harboring bacteria that was causing my fevers. I was hoping to get both ports removed but Dr. Wade would only approve removing the tri-port. The original port, which was on the opposite side, was inserted below the skin, so it was not exposed to air or bacteria. For now, it would remain.

After taking the oral meds for the two blood clots for a week or so, we became aware that the Warfarin conflicted with some of the other medications I was taking. I was having some negative reactions with itching and peeling skin, and everything pointed towards the Warfarin as the cause. Because the doctors required me to take blood thinners for the two blood clots, the only solution was to get another blood thinning drug called Lovenox that could be administered only by injections in my stomach. The first one was at the local cancer care center, and they told me I would have to come back there every day to receive a shot unless I did it myself. The last thing I wanted was to have to go to a medical facility daily, so I had the nurse show me how to do it. From that point on, I purchased the shots from my local pharmacy for self-injection.

Since I used to have a phobia for needles, this was a huge challenge for me! I reasoned that this is what I had to do, and after everything I had been through to this point, the thought of a needle going into me was not a big deal. My mother was the most shocked that I would give myself an injection. She liked to remind me that when I was a child, it took three people to hold me down to get vaccinations. I did remember going to the pediatrician's office as a child and feeling very queasy knowing that I would probably get stuck. Even as a teenager and young adult, I would feel sick to my stomach when giving blood or getting an injection. That was all gone now.

My routine was going into the bathroom, sitting on the toilet stool, and pinching about an inch of skin in my abdomen while I gently inserted the needle. I learned that the medicine had to slowly be injected into my body, then wait a little while before removing the needle. Otherwise, most of the Lovenox comes back out when the needle is removed! Apparently, it takes some time for the surrounding tissues to absorb the injected medicine. As time went on, it became a little easier, but watching that needle enter and having to leave it in me long enough for the medicine to be absorbed never became something with which I was totally at ease. I also found out that I had to be extremely careful where I put the shot. One day I hit a small blood vessel and when I was sitting in my chair after giving myself an injection, Joyce commented that I had bled through the band-aid. I had about a three-inch diameter blood stain on my tee shirt and had to apply pressure for several minutes to get it to stop bleeding. Obviously, it was one of the pitfalls of using a blood-thinning medication.

May 7, 2013 was Day 90 after my transplant, and I was back at Barnes in St. Louis getting more labs and a checkup from Dr. Westervelt. Getting rid of the fevers was a major sign that I was not having graft versus host rejection of the transplant, but I was still dealing with itchy skin rashes which is a typical transplant rejection issue or possibly a reaction to some of the daily medications.

By the second week of May 2013, my skin rashes and itching got worse again and I started taking an oral 5mg prednisone dose. Back when I was readmitted to Barnes in March, they put me on 80mg of prednisone every day and then after the skin rashes got better, I was taken off this high dose with a fast taper. One thing I have learned about my body is that it would respond well to lower doses of medications than what was typically given, and slow tapers were better to minimize side effects of the medications.

Since the prednisone helped in March, I felt the low dose was helping me. After some conferring, both doctors in Decatur and St. Louis said that 5mg was too low to be therapeutic. I tried to convince them that it was helping, but they did not believe me. They recommended stopping the prednisone and just using steroid cream for the itching. Of course, my skin rashes and itching got worse. Within just a few days the doctor wanted to put me on a daily 50mg dose of prednisone, but we compromised at 30mg. 50mg of prednisone would bring back the shaking and sleeplessness, and I did not want to return to that. All the while, I was praying these skin issues were not a graft- vs-host response. I was also back to having low-grade fevers occasionally.

As we progressed from May into June 2013, my white blood counts dropped to dangerously low levels which I was sure was due to the 30mg prednisone. This was emotionally hard for me to be isolated from people, and the negative thoughts had to be dealt with again. To combat the low white blood count and ANC, I had to add Neupogen to my daily regime. Neupogen is an injectable drug, so this meant TWO shots a day in my stomach: Neupogen for the low white blood count and Lovenox for the blood clots. I was able to stop the Neupogen after three days because it kicked my white blood overall count and ANC way up. This allowed me to go back to a more normal life routine and tapering of the prednisone began again.

The frustration over this endless merry-go-round was reaching epic levels. I voiced all this to Dr. Wade here in Decatur, and after reviewing the lab results from June 3, he felt that my skin rashes and itching were not due to my body rejecting the transplant but due to the Bactrim antibiotic that I was taking daily. He stated that if I were having a transplant rejection issue, several of my other blood tests parameters would be out of whack. Since I was having the skin rashes and itching and my Eosinophils (the cells that measure allergic reaction) were high, he was convinced it was an allergic reaction to this antibiotic. Could this finally be the solution??

Yes, Dr. Wade solved this problem yet again. Several days after replacing this antibiotic, my skin cleared up completely. I was frustrated that my Barnes medical personnel did not figure this out much earlier and instead put me on the 30mg prednisone that was not needed if the allergy had been discovered sooner. It felt great to stop itching but greater yet knowing that my body was not rejecting my new bone marrow. However, the prednisone can suppress the immune system, and my white count was again declining as well as having several new issues.

During the time of being on the 30mg prednisone, I experienced about a week of some serious digestive distress. We joked within the family that it was due to some long-expired hot sauce my mom had in her kitchen, but a stool culture came back positive for a C-diff infection. C-diff is a serious opportunistic critter that can rear up due to too many antibiotics/low immune system and not enough healthy bacteria in my system. To remedy this, I started on yet another drug, Flagyl, on Monday, as well as super-duper pro-biotics to hopefully "recolonize" my gut with the good stuff. Earlier on, I could not take the probiotics, because with the low counts I had before, even "good" bacteria were bad for me. What a quandary I continued to find myself in! Of course, more Neupogen shots were needed to boost that white blood count again as well as semi-isolation until the counts rebounded. I felt I was exiting one ride only to get right back on another but was determined to see a turn-around soon.

With my skin cleared up and having my white blood count at better levels, I was able to finally be around family and friends at several events during June 2013. By June 18, I decided to go on-site to check on some of my computer customers. This was done to begin getting myself back into my IT work. I reviewed my list of existing computer clients and decided to take back about half of the workload that I had previously managed.

As difficult as this was, I knew it was the right decision. My energy levels were much lower, (as was my immune system) and I wanted to be with Joyce more to help her with the garment business. Since being on my own in 2005, my computer business had grown to the point where I could not realistically service all my clients in a timely manner with my health issues. I decided to be proactive and let some of my customers stay with the computer companies that had been servicing them for the past six months.

I could safely be in public, but I really did not want to push it too much. Touching keyboards is a good way to contract germs. Although Joyce armed me with sanitizing wipes and hand sanitizer to use while out and about, I knew the overall risk to my health was still formidable. I genuinely wanted a *reboot*, and this would allow me more flexibility to have more time to spend with Joyce, other family members, and friends.

After these last 11 months, being with those closest to me really lifted me up emotionally. Our area has a women's cancer survivor walk the last Saturday of June, and they asked if I could play piano at that event. This was the first time I would publicly perform, and the event was outside, so I felt my immune system was safe. Several people there who knew of my journey spoke encouragement and told me they had been praying for me. It was a HUGE boost to my emotional well-being to finally be around people again.

I was back in St. Louis the first week of July to get lab work and a checkup with Dr. Westervelt. He was pleased with my blood counts and stated that he would be happy if my blood counts continued at their current levels (white blood count 2.8 and ANC was 2,153). Dr. Westervelt also recommended increased dosages on the Mepron antibiotic and Tacrolimus. We checked with Dr. Wade on these changes and researched them ourselves. The Mepron increase was fine, but because the Tacrolimus is an immuno-suppressant, we were concerned about their recommendation to double the amount. Tacrolimus is to prevent GVHD (Graft-vs-Host-Disease) and even though my current Tacrolimus levels are lower than they like to see, I was not having any symptoms of GVHD. Again, we negotiated a smaller increase on Tacrolimus, just like we did on the prednisone. The prednisone taper was also continuing, and I was now down to 17.5mg per day.

I finished the Flagyl on July 4, declaring my "independence" from the C-diff infection. It had to be confirmed with the lab, and test results came back negative. I then continued taking the probiotic every day to ward off any future digestive issues. Unfortunately, though, the increased Tacrolimus caused my white blood count and ANC to drop to the point where I needed to give myself a Neupogen injection for a couple of days. Despite this, we were able to go up to Chicago to visit our daughter in early July. Upon returning, I continued to ramp up work on computers and garments. Beginning that month, I started light regular workouts at the local gym and getting massages again. I had been doing what I could at home for physical fitness but now was able to get back to other activities. We got our granddaughter for more frequent visits at our home and took her to see my mother. Joyce and I were able to go out with friends and see neighbors; however, we still took extreme precautions to protect my immune system.

Throughout this whole ordeal, we were in regular communication with our local church and other Christian friends, and in June and July I had several lunches with my closest buddies. What a huge encouragement they were to me through their prayers and my being able to share with them what I was going through. Their care and concern showed me that I was not going through this alone even though at times I was so physically isolated. Utilizing the Neupogen shots when needed allowed my counts to stay at a level where I was able to be careful while being around other people.

Because of that, I felt it was time for me to get back to playing piano again with the band at my local church. I could not wait! Being a part of the praise band was a huge part of my life, and I had been unable to do this for a long time. I was placed on the schedule for August 4/5, and August 10/11. Walking into the first practice in our church lifted me up in ways I cannot describe. I was overwhelmed with my fellow musicians, singers and tech crew who were excited to see me come back. As I took my place at the grand piano, a flood of emotions welled up inside of me. How good is my Father who brought me back from the brink of death to have me play music again in His House? As my hands moved over those keys, I could hardly focus on the music. Practice was great, but when I got on the platform in front of several hundred people on August 4, I was choking back the tears of joy and gratitude. A small part of me finally felt like things were becoming normal again.

Another exciting thing was that my pastor called me up front during the three weekend services on August 4 and 5 to let people know the reason I had been absent for over six months. What a testimony to our Lord on how He can provide a miraculous recovery! God was not done yet with my return. During the Saturday evening service, we had a technical problem with the video that was to play during communion. Our pastor asked me if I could play a song during the communion time, which I was extremely happy to do. My wife's favorite hymn (and one of mine too) is Great Is Thy Faithfulness, and I played that during communion at the Saturday evening service. How appropriate for me to play this at the first service back!

As I was playing this song and trying to keep my composure, I glanced out at the congregation and saw my wife and my pastor's wife crying. I immediately asked the Holy Spirit to help me keep playing because I could not contain my emotions. He helped me complete the song and I went backstage and let it all go. A release of emotions came forth as the tears flowed down my cheeks and all I could think of was how awesome is my Father! I went out to sit with my wife during the sermon and she also had been crying a lot. For those few moments we just held onto each other and enjoyed the presence of our Lord as Pastor preached. God allowed me to overcome so much and was so good to me even in the darker days.

After playing piano again at church the following weekend, we headed to St. Louis on Monday to spend the night at the Parkway Hotel prior to a full day of tests and a checkup at Barnes the next day. Since we arrived early, we were able to spend some time with another stem cell transplant survivor and his wife we met when I was there. It was good to see them and hear how they are coping with the aftermath of his transplant. We all had a list of issues that we were dealing with and encouraged each other to keep our spirits up and continue to persevere.

We got to the lab at 7am for the fasting blood draw from my Power Port, then went to breakfast across the street at the local St. Louis Bread Company. At 9am, I got my eleventh bone marrow biopsy from Greg, the same tech who performed the last three biopsies. He was very experienced and normally quick to get it done with a minimal amount of pain. However, on this one, when he went to aspirate the marrow, I came off the table due to the intense pain level. The local anesthetic helps, but when they get into the bone marrow, sometimes it becomes extremely severe and the local doesn't help. I needed a few minutes on the table when he was through to refresh myself mentally before journeying to the next test location. Next stop was a 10am appointment with our Barnes oncologist nurse practitioner to review the lab test results, and my ANC was just over 1,000.

Since I was still in a study which administers chemo after

the transplant as a prevention measure, I was to receive a Rituxan chemo treatment in the Barnes infusion area. This study was looking at the effect of getting chemo after an allogeneic stem cell transplant and its ability to prevent recurrence and GVHD. Being in an infusion area again caused many anxious emotions and took me back to the not so distant past of getting chemo treatments prior to the transplant. Fortunately, I brought a customer's laptop to work on while I was getting my treatment, which helped take my mind off getting the chemo through my Power Port as well as ignore another patient in the infusion area that was getting sick from her treatment. Some memories are just not worth revisiting, and this ranked right up there.

After completing my chemo treatment, I ate lunch downstairs in the cafeteria/lobby area while enjoying some local musicians. A father and son sat at the same table and since the dad had an Illini ball cap and son had a Cubs ball cap, we were able to share our perspectives on our teams. I found out they were from Champaign, Illinois (where I went to college), and the son has been battling various health issues ever since he was born (he looked to be in his 20s now). This really impacted me that I was blessed to enjoy good health for my first 50 years, and I felt empathy for this young man who had never known any time in his life without dealing with physical health issues. As much as I despised the thought, two more Rituxan treatments were scheduled for November 2013 and February 2014.

On Thursday, August 15, I got a call from Barnes stating that there still was no leukemia found in the bone marrow sample that had been drawn on Tuesday and that my new marrow was creating all three types of blood cells (red/white/platelets). The good news kept coming. On Friday of that week, I was at my local hospital getting the Power Port that had been placed in my right chest all the way back in June 2010 removed. Unlike my high anxiety in 2010, I was very relaxed going into the operating room and had already dealt with the removal of the Hickman catheter.

When the doctor injected the local anesthetic, he did not wait long enough for it to take complete effect. He grabbed the scalpel and as he made the initial cut into my right chest, I felt the knife cut through my skin which really hurt! I took a deep breath and calmly told the doctor that I felt that incision and that we needed to wait a little time for the numbing to take effect. No one wants to spend more time at the hospital than needed, but gee doc, give it a few minutes—ouch! He injected more lidocaine into my chest and neck and then took a short break to allow the medicine to work. Again, like the previous tri-port removal, my body had some scar tissue around this hardware that had grown into the port itself. After some tugging and extra cuts, this Power Port was completely removed, and everything was sewn up. I was now finally free from being a cyborg and with no hardware in my body, I was also able to stop the daily Lovenox shots.

The next day we celebrated my mother-in-law's 96th birthday. She had overcome several of her own health problems this year, and although now living in a nursing home that Joyce had her transferred to the day before I was going to St. Louis for the stem cell transplant, she was doing much better. This party was for much more than just a birthday, this was a huge celebration for both of us coming through an exceedingly difficult year.

The last weekend of the month Joyce and I also went away for the weekend to a bed and breakfast in Keokuk, Iowa. It felt great to go out of town without any scheduled medical appointments or procedures. We stood on a hill and overlooked the Mississippi River while a late summer festival was going on a short distance away. The sights and sounds of that festival were like a soothing balm on the emotional wounds I'd weathered over the last six months. Finally, I was able to travel somewhere other than St. Louis for check-ups, and the flood of encouraging thoughts continued to lift me up.

All the while, I continued the slow taper of my daily prednisone dosage and dropped it to 10mg. If no GVHD symptoms appeared, I would continue tapering off the prednisone. This would be the first medication to be stopped, then hopefully other medications could be reduced and eventually removed. I continued weekly blood tests to monitor my white blood and ANC counts that were still bouncing around quite a bit and running lower than we wanted, but the Neupogen was available when I needed it.

My September appointment with Dr. Wade consisted of reviewing a list of immunizations that he wanted me to get. One of the "side-effects" of having all new bone marrow and blood, is that my old immune system was eliminated and completely reset. As he explained it, any previous immunizations were wiped out and in order to be protected from the typical diseases, all childhood shots would have to be completed again. This is a topic that doctors do not all agree upon.

The oncologist for one of my stem cell transplant friends would not allow him to get any immunizations due to a concern about causing graft versus host (GVHD) issues. However, since I had not exhibited any symptoms of GVHD (my body rejecting the transplant), he wanted me to start getting these shots if my blood counts were high enough to do so. The first one to get was a flu shot on September 24.

Within one week, my ANC plunged to 765. After giving myself a Neupogen shot on two consecutive days, the count was checked four days later, and it had dropped down to 684. I administered three more Neupogen shots over the next three days (one each day into my stomach area). This got the counts to 3780 so Dr. Wade gave me the approval to go on a weekend trip the first weekend of October with a group of family and friends to tour wineries in Southern Illinois. We were about an hour from home when we called in to get the previous days' counts. We were shocked when the nurse told us it had fallen to 805 on the ANC. Even worse, we had not packed any additional Neupogen shots for the weekend, and whenever it got below 1000, Dr. Wade wanted me to get a shot. Because the Cancer Care center was one of our embroidery clients, we knew they had an auxiliary location in Centralia, IL. This was slightly off the path to our destination but was still better than turning around at the point we now were on the trip. The nurses called ahead to the location, and a little after 2pm I had my Neupogen shot and was ready to resume travel. Once again, we had a lovely getaway with family members and good friends as we enjoyed the early fall air. Even a rogue thunderstorm on Saturday could not dampen my spirit.

Instead of coming home on Sunday, we headed west to St. Louis and spent time with our transplant survivor friend and his wife. We met at a local restaurant for lunch that Sunday. After hearing him go through the litany of GVHD symptoms he was experiencing (eyes so dry one had to be partially sewn shut, numbness in his feet and legs, and severe digestive issues) I knew how blessed I was to only endure an occasional Neupogen shot. He looked frail and I could tell these ongoing health problems were taking a toll on him. I realized that I, too, could be facing lifelong issues with rejection of the transplant, but so far, everything was only centered around my low white blood and absolute neutrophil counts.

The other person we saw was the brother-in-law of a close friend who was getting ready to receive an allogeneic stem cell transplant at Barnes. We went on Monday morning to see him and his wife on the eighth floor of the same building where I had received my transplant earlier this year. I wondered as we approached the building how I would react to going back into this facility. Would Joyce and I have an emotional struggle? Surprisingly, Joyce and I both were able to go back in feeling very calm and blessed.

We spent over an hour visiting with this man and his wife and answering a lot of their questions based on us having just been through this process eight months earlier. They were also encouraged to see how well I was doing which gave them hope for a positive outcome. After we left his room, we went down to the fifth floor to check in with the medical personnel that had taken care of me. We got to see nurses, techs and cleaning people that had taken care of me. They were so happy to see one of their recent patients back and doing great.

As I shared earlier, the stem cell transplant is a last resort for people with serious blood cancers, and many recipients deal with lifelong rejection issues or just do not survive the process. This is a difficult environment for the Barnes personnel to work in, as well as a tough process to endure as a patient. Looking out those same windows I was reminded of several months ago when I was in my deepest despair and how my Father got me through this valley (Psalm 23). Instead of struggling with being back on the fifth floor, I felt elated and leaving the facility with Joyce was like a victory lap.

The next day I was back home doing computer work and stopped by the local cancer care center for blood work. With no ports to use now, it was back to getting stuck in the arms. Given everything I had experienced so far, my old needle phobia was long gone. Again, my low white/ANC blood counts prompted three Neupogen shots over the following three days (at a cost of $500 each). Thank God for good insurance! This was also my last week for tapering off prednisone which was the first step for me to finally eliminate one of my prescription medications. The Neupogen shots were effective in elevating my white/ANC blood counts, but the effects did not last very long. On October 8th, my white/ANC blood counts were 1.8/684, and after three days of Neupogen shots, they were 6.3/3780. By October 18, these counts were back down to 2.3/805. However, with no signs of GVHD issues and being off prednisone, several more of my daily prescription medications were reduced. Given my low white/ANC counts, hand sanitizer and Clorox wipes were used frequently, and I could not see my granddaughter since she had started pre-school and was dealing with her own illnesses. The Barnes medical people also told me to hold off any more immunizations at this time since the flu shot caused such a rapid decline in my counts. I occasionally had localized skin itching, but it was nothing like before and could be alleviated with the steroid cream when needed.

I returned to the Barnes West County lab in early November for labs and a check-up. I was also supposed to receive the third Rituxan chemo treatment as part of the study that I was participating in (one treatment every three months after the transplant). My white/ANC blood counts were 2.2/800 and the minimum ANC was 1,000 to receive the Rituxan. They rescheduled the treatment for November 19, and more Neupogen shots were administered three days prior to assure my counts would be high enough.

Prior to leaving for St. Louis, Joyce researched the impact of Rituxan chemo on patients' white/ANC blood counts (neutropenia). She found research articles suggesting a strong correlation with Rituxan causing low white/ANC counts. We both prayed about this and I decided that I would not receive any more Rituxan to try and reverse the neutropenia issues that I had been struggling with. When we met with Dr. Westervelt and staff at Barnes, they did not seem surprised at our findings. Although he did not think the Rituxan was a culprit in my neutropenia struggle, he agreed with our decision because I was not having GVHD issues. I was also able to eliminate both the anti-fungal medicine and the antibiotic medicine I had been taking daily. Although these were not known to cause low blood counts, the elimination of them could possibly change the outcomes on my future labs and we were hopeful they would. Only the anti- viral drug remained, and I knew that was to prevent me from getting shingles.

Also, to avoid the urgency of using the Neupogen only when my counts were already in the danger zone, the doctor recommended that I give myself two Neupogen shots each week for a month to try and maintain healthy levels. Our hope was that between stopping the Rituxan, doing the regular Neupogen shots and reducing maintenance medications, my white/ANC blood counts would stabilize and eventually increase.

On our 24th wedding anniversary, 11/24/13, we went to Southern Illinois for four days and stayed in a small cabin by ourselves. We steered clear of crowds but enjoyed so much that such a scenic area has to offer. Once again, it was nice to go on a trip without having to visit medical facilities and get poked, stuck, cut, drilled, or receive whatever chemicals in my body. With my compromised immune system, we had to avoid Thanksgiving with most of my family due to other people battling illnesses. As much as I wanted to be there, the risks were far too great. As a result, Joyce and I took my mother-in-law out for dinner at a local restaurant by ourselves.

December went well. I avoided getting any sickness (taking all the precautions and avoiding crowds) and was able to play music at church on two weekends and on Christmas Eve. During alternate weekends, Joyce and I would sit up in the balcony to avoid the crowd. Hearing the chorus of coughing below us, we knew that was a wise decision that still allowed us to attend weekly worship. Instead of shaking hands, we did and continue to do elbow bumps. Some people react surprised to this, but I just tell them that I am a cancer survivor with an impaired immune system. Everyone seems to understand that, and most congratulate me on being a survivor.

The weekly blood tests continued to show relatively low white blood counts/ ANC. Even still, the doctor reduced my two weekly Neupogen shots to one at the beginning of December. The ANC hovered around the 700-900 range and the red and platelets had been holding steady at the low end on the normal range. My goal for 2014 was for all three types to elevate into more normal ranges. I would continue to get weekly blood tests at Cancer Care in Decatur.

I also was able to be with the entire family on Christmas

Day. Seeing my granddaughter was the highlight of that. My youngest daughter Jodi was pregnant and due in February, so another grandchild would enrich my life. There was much to look forward to in the coming year.

Being able to exercise, work, play music, and be around people kept me from thinking about how difficult 2013 was. I do remember that there were times earlier in the year when I did not know if I would see 2014. Not only did I make it to 2014, but God blessed me with no significant health problems from the transplant. The best Christmas gift I received was the absence of any leukemia in my body! I so appreciated every day when I felt like getting out of bed, eating tasty food, and having energy to exercise and work. You do not realize how much these routine things impact you until they are not functioning right!

Joyce and I continued to work more together on the embroidery business. I was grateful God gave us wisdom on me taking back fewer computer clients, because we had a lot of embroidery work to do in the fourth quarter of 2013. When I did go out on computer calls, people at the companies I visited were very gracious and understood that I had to be careful to protect myself from illnesses. 2013 was undoubtedly a year of great impact on my physical, mental, and spiritual health. Without the prayers and support, I don't believe I would have made it through.

Look Up

Chapter 10

White Blood Count Battle (Jan 2014 – Dec 2014)

2014!! A new year with lots of new promise ahead. Emotionally, I felt myself recovering as the isolation I was forced to endure in 2013 was slowly giving way to more and more face-to-face interactions with people. I was also back home and doing computer and garment work, playing piano, and working out on a regular basis. With my low white/ANC blood counts, we were careful to avoid crowds and anyone who exhibited any signs of illness. Barnes medical personnel were adamant about my being susceptible to getting sick; any common cold or communicable disease could cause me serious problems. They really stressed that the Absolute Neutrophil Count (ANC) needed to be over 1,500, but my local oncologist was not as concerned. His view was that those neutrophil cells were in my system like parked police cars just waiting to be dispatched when an infection occurred. With no infection happening, his perspective was that there would be fewer in the blood stream and the lower ANC was not necessarily an ineffective immune system. So far, I had not gotten sick, but we were taking many steps to avoid environments that could be conducive to me picking up some illness or infection. The medical community classifies ANC levels this way:

Mild Neutropenia (1,000 – 1,499) Minimal Risk of Infection

Moderate Neutropenia (500 – 999) Moderate Risk of Infection

Severe Neutropenia (<500) Severe Risk of Infection

I started 2014 with an ANC over 1,000 so no Neupogen shot was needed the first week. However, the ANC dropped the next two weeks to 680 and 510, so I did one Neupogen shot each week. By mid-month, I was back down at Barnes West County and my doctor there, who had continued to reduce my other maintenance medications after the prednisone was stopped in September 2013, reviewed my final two maintenance medications. Since I was not having any rejection issues with my new bone marrow and blood, Tacrolimus, the anti-rejection prescription, was stopped. That left only Valacyclovir, an anti-viral prescription, as the final remaining maintenance medication. With a compromised immune system, the risk of getting shingles was higher, and that was the primary purpose of that drug. With just having a single maintenance daily prescription, we were hoping that my white/ANC blood counts would increase and stabilize. Many of the drugs used to stabilize my system after the transplant could also depress my body's ability to create healthy immune-fighting cells. Even with the latest reduction of meds, over the next several weeks my white/ANC counts continued to be low and I had to take a couple of Neupogen shots to keep my counts from dropping to dangerous levels.

I celebrated my one-year anniversary of the transplant on Thursday 02/06/14, treating myself to a massage then getting a blood test and giving myself a Neupogen shot later in the day. Because I was at the one-year mark, I had several days of medical tests to determine the status of my new bone marrow. CT scans with contrast were completed on 02/10/14 and Dr. Wade reviewed these scans the next day. All scans were all clear and no traces of any cancer were detected. We then went back down to Barnes in St. Louis on Friday, February 14, 2014, and I got more blood work and the twelfth bone marrow biopsy.

To say that I was tired of this procedure would be an understatement. Although the pain was brief, it was by far the most intense pain I have ever endured in my entire life. To make matters worse, the tech that performed the biopsy stated that he had to drill through some scar tissue to extract bone marrow because I had so many of these.

I still just got a local anesthetic and endured the excruciating pain with my normal routine of Lamaze breathing and squeezing my outstretched forearms as needed. After getting an even dozen of them over the past five years, I told people who asked me if I got used to it that "no, I never got used to it." I learned how to cope with the pain and not fear it. I knew it was going to hurt but having experienced so many of them and other painful procedures during this battle with cancer, I was able to "press into" the pain rather than try to avoid it. Just as I learned that only my human body I am walking around in could get cancer, I also realized that pain from this body was something that I could also separate myself from in my mind, will and emotions.

I still felt the pain but by thinking of it in this way I was able to endure the pain without the high anxiety and emotional stress because I knew it was temporary. Although the bone marrow biopsy showed no traces of cancer and that my marrow was still fully ingrafted with my donor's cells, the blood work came back with an ANC of 400, so yet another Neupogen shot was given before I left the facility. As the nurse was about to give me the Neupogen shot, I asked her to give me the syringe. She looked at me with a puzzled expression, and I told her that I had been giving myself these shots many times since the bone marrow transplant, so she gave me the syringe and I administered the shot to my abdominal area. I even got a compliment from the nurse telling me that I performed the injection correctly. Five years prior, I could not even tolerate the thought of getting a shot, and now I was giving them to myself like a pro. Funny how God gives you strength for the smallest of things.

We returned home that day, but on the afternoon of Sunday February 16, our daughter went into labor. She lived in the Chicago area and we were able to make it there prior to our grandson's arrival later that evening. Being in a hospital, especially during the height of cold and flu season was challenging, but I wore the N95 mask to protect my immune system. I kept some distance from people, but we were happy to be there for his birth and this wonderful occasion. Truthfully, I was also relieved to go into a hospital as a visitor. The birth went well, and Jodi and new baby Silas were fine afterward.

During the following month, I continued weekly blood tests and administered multiple Neupogen shots ($500.00 each) over this time, because my ANC count was hovering around the 500-800 level. When I returned to Barnes in mid-March, my doctor told us about a relatively new donor stem cell boost procedure that could possibly get my white/ANC blood counts up. This procedure injects more of my original donor's cells (there were still stem cells left over from the original transplant in February 2013 that were frozen at Barnes) into my body without any chemo or other medications. My doctor began the approval process with my insurance company because this stem cell boost had just been added as an approved medical procedure the previous October. By the end of March, my ANC dropped to 240, the lowest level since being in the hospital over a year ago. To try and bring it up, I gave myself two Neupogen shots in three days and had to continue to isolate myself from family members and other people to avoid picking up any illnesses. To make matters worse, we also got a denial from my insurance company for the stem cell boost. Their reason was that the current use of Neupogen as needed was working fine and the stem cell boost was still experimental in their eyes. From my perspective, this was not acceptable and certainly not sustainable.

Having to get weekly and sometimes more frequent blood tests and giving myself Neupogen shots multiple times a month at $500.00 each was costing quite a bit and could be avoided if this stem cell boost worked. Reaching my deductible helped with the overall cost, but the insurance company wanted to limit the number of shots to only once a week.

I also could not start getting my immunizations until my white/ANC blood count stabilized because the immunizations always caused a slight downward trend as my body fought to create new antibodies. This made me more susceptible to getting diseases that could be thwarted with getting these standard immunizations. One serious illness and hospital stay would be more than the $20K for the stem cell boost.

Due to these continued low white blood counts, our St. Louis medical team continued to try and get Blue Cross insurance to approve this "donor cell boost." Two more denials came, and the Barnes medical team told us that they had never won an appeal with BCBS for this type of procedure. After much prayer from us, our many people at church and followers on my CaringBridge site, Joyce was able to leverage her Allstate claims adjuster experience to find the correct medical codes and information from various websites and an updated BCBS policy manual to our Barnes medical team. The codes for the exact procedure I needed were added to the BCBS policy manual on June 1 of 2014. Our nurse coordinator's supervisor also got involved and spearheaded the effort.

Once again, we filed an appeal, and Dr. Westervelt, my transplant doctor, did a peer to peer review with a Blue

Cross doctor and thankfully it was an oncologist he spoke with. We were told that the peer to peer reviews could be done with any random doctor, and the circumstances of it being an oncologist was the best possible scenario. After three months of working on this, the appeals department of my insurance company called on June 11 to say the appeal was successful and they sent a letter giving the approval. Three months of diligence and prayer had paid off!

While all this was happening, I had submitted the paperwork to the National Marrow Donor Program to try and connect with my stem cell donor. They do not allow the survivor to try to connect with the donor until at least a year from the stem cell transplant to ensure that the survivor is doing well. The first week in June I got an email from my Barnes Hospital transplant coordinator with my donor's contact information. He was in the Navy, and his phone area code was from Los Angeles. I sent him an email on June 4 thanking him for his donation and got a reply on June 5. He was at sea, but he said that he was not available via phone since he was in deployment. I was hoping to make future contact with him. Getting a face to face with the man whose cells saved my life would be an awesome achievement in the scheme of this whole journey.

On June 13 we were back at Barnes West County in St. Louis for my monthly exam and blood work. With the approval of the donor stem cell boost, they added an EKG and chest X-Ray in preparation for the stem cell boost. During the next two weeks, my ANC count dropped to 263 and 288 so, once again, I had to give myself multiple

Neupogen shots. With these low counts, we pushed hard to get this stem cell boost scheduled ASAP. The medical staff had scheduled the stem cell boost for June 24 and told me that it would be done as an out-patient procedure. However, since I was the first patient to get this procedure approved, there was much confusion within the facility as to whether this should be done as an inpatient or outpatient procedure. Because of the inability to get that resolved by the original target date, the stem cell boost procedure was pushed out to July 1 and was supposed to be done as an outpatient. We had conquered the hurdle of the approval, but now the facility was causing the delay because they weren't sure how to code and proceed with what I was having done.

As Joyce and I were driving across the Mississippi River on June 30, enroute to the hotel we were checking in the day before the procedure, we got a call from Dr. Westervelt from Barnes stating that I had to go back to the fifth floor and be an in-patient to get the stem cell boost due to their internal business decision. We were terribly upset and concerned about me getting this stem cell boost done because my insurance company had approved this as an out-patient procedure only. My doctor told us that as long as I am in and out prior to spending a complete 24-hour period, that would work with the insurance company requirement for being an out-patient procedure. With $20K on the line, I wanted to make sure that this was going to be completely covered. Needless to say, anxiety was high as we checked into the Parkway Hotel next to Barnes Hospital that evening. I fasted that evening as I would be required to undergo a PICC line placement early the next day.

Here is what happened on July 1, 2014:

Lab-6:30AM—this went fine and because the hotel has a walkway that connects to the hospital, I was able to do the lab and then go back to the room to get Joyce.

PICC Line Placement-7:30AM – 9:00AM

As they checked me to place the line, a narrowing was found in my right neck vein. Later during this day, a doppler was used to check my right neck vein for blood clots. Fortunately, there was no clot and this narrowing was due to scar tissue from old Power Port. The PICC line stands for Peripherally Inserted Central Catheter and is a long tube that is inserted in the jugular vein that carries blood to the heart. It would carry the medications and cells once the infusion process started.

I was admitted as inpatient (23-hour) at 1:45PM in Room 5938. Knowing I was going back on the fifth floor again was mentally challenging for me given what I had endured last year. There definitely was a PTSD component to exiting the elevator and walking down those hallways as I had done so many times when I was an inpatient during the transplant. The cell processing started at 2:10PM so 2 hours of fluids through the line in my neck was started. The meds included Benadryl, Tylenol, and Ativan.

One of the RN's brought in the package of cells a little after 4pm. She said the doctor had to be the one to administer them, and the doctor had been paged. Several minutes went by, and the doctor did not respond. Joyce asked the RN how long the cells remain viable after they are thawed, and she said they begin to degrade immediately, and need to be infused within a half-hour. Fifteen minutes later there still was no response from the doctor after the second page, so Joyce went out in the hallway to try and locate the doctor. Joyce was able to locate her, and within just a few minutes, the doctor was in my room and the infusion of the white blood stem cells began just before 4:30pm.

Because it was only my white blood cells that were deficient, the stem cells were processed prior to my infusion to remove the red cells and platelets. The doctor told us this process required very high-tech equipment to separate these out, which was a big reason for the high cost of the procedure.

The PICC line had to be removed prior to my discharge, and because there had been such a delay in everything that day, the people in the department that inserted the line had already left for the day. We were told a doctor on the floor would remove the line.

By 5:30 I was showing no signs of distress and Joyce buzzed for the doctor. She was concerned because the doctor that came into the room was a very small (probably 90-100 pounds) female who spoke somewhat broken English. She told Joyce she was going to remove the line from the vein in my neck and then apply pressure to get the bleeding to stop. Joyce said all she could envision was blood squirting everywhere as she watched this lady lean on me for five minutes with all her weight to stop the bleeding. When she stood up, there was no bleeding at all, and a bandage was placed on my neck where the PICC line had been.

I was discharged at 6:00PM. Joyce wheeled me back to the Parkway Hotel although I do not remember much of what happened after being discharged because of the pre-meds. I was pretty much out of it. Joyce fed me part of a sandwich and I went straight to bed. When I awoke the next day, the meds were out of my system, we drove home, and I was already back working by the end of that day.

On July 3, I got a blood test at Cancer Care in Decatur and my ANC was at 470 so I gave myself a Neupogen shot that evening. We were told that it would take some time to see any effects of the stem cell boost because those newly infused cells would need time to engraft. We were thrilled when I had blood work done on July 10 with an ANC of 1,950 with an overall white blood count of 3800 (4,000 is the bottom of normal WBC range and I was just under that). This result allowed me to go to every other week for CBC blood tests. I was back in St Louis on August 8 for blood tests and a checkup, and Dr. Westervelt said that he was hoping for a homerun with the stem cell boost, but we got a double. My ANC counts were higher, but I was still below normal range. That could improve with time, but with the higher ANC counts, he gave me the go ahead to start getting immunizations. I continued taking my last maintenance medication, the anti-viral Valacyclovir, for now.

To celebrate, we stayed the weekend in St. Louis and visited with a couple whose husband also had an allogeneic stem cell transplant. His transplant was about seven months after mine, and we were able to help them deal with the difficult process and prayed for them and his recovery. He also was doing very well from his transplant and was not experiencing any rejection issues. (Prayer works!!)

With my higher white blood counts, I was also able to go to my dentist on September 25 and get a teeth cleaning and check-up. Prior to my stem cell boost, my low white blood count and compromised immune system could expose me to a serious infection from a dental cleaning since this procedure releases bacteria in the mouth. It felt great to get my teeth cleaned and I fortunately did not have any dental issues. Who would have thought that a visit to the dentist would be something to look forward to?

By the end of September, I got my flu shot and did not get sick from it. My ANC counts jumped up to 2695 in early October, but then plummeted to 500 on October 10. Since I was in St. Louis getting labs and a checkup on that day with the nurse practitioner, I gave myself a Neupogen shot and talked with her about why my ANC dropped over 2,000 points in a week. She blamed the flu shot for this sudden rise then fall due to my body's overreaction to the flu vaccine. I now knew to closely monitor my ANC counts as I proceeded with getting more immunizations. This was the second year in a row that the flu shot caused my WBC to tumble.

While in St. Louis we met with a finance manager at Barnes reviewing the in-patient versus out-patient problems with the stem cell boost and the delays caused by the hospital not knowing how to proceed. He explained that they were having to do the in- patient admission to absorb the cost of this procedure, and I was the first patient at Barnes to get the stem cell boost done as a normal medical procedure, not as part of a clinical trial. With me being the first, they were still working out internal business decisions for this procedure. I was a pioneer of sorts with this newly approved procedure, but the delays still caused a lot of angst as the issues between the hospital and insurance company were resolved.

That following weekend, I was playing piano with my church band and the pastor had me speak with him during his sermon to share my journey through the leukemia battle. As I shared what all I had been through so far, I was able thank everyone for supporting me and my family. Getting through this process and continuing to battle with the recovery challenges is a team effort and all prayers and messages of encouragements were vital to help us overcome. Several people came up to me afterward and told me how much I had inspired them by coming back and playing piano. Seeing me up front encouraged many of my Christian brothers and sisters who were struggling through their own trials. I was now seeing a bigger picture to this battle with leukemia which got me to focus even more on God's perspective and plan in my situation. If I am being watched by others on how I handle this challenge, was I giving them a positive example?

Even though my health insurance company had sent both me and the hospital the approval letter from their appeals department in June for my stem-cell boost procedure, when the medical bills were submitted by Barnes Hospital, the Explanation-Of-Benefits (EOBs) showed that these claims were denied by my insurance company. I immediately contacted the claims department when this denial was received in late July.

Each month from July through November, I would contact them, and they said they would review the claim and secure the approval letter I already had in hand. After each conversation, a couple of weeks would go by and they would deny it again. I told them every time that I had an approval letter from their appeals department, but no one there could verify that their appeals department had approved this procedure. I tried to contact the person who had signed my approval letter, but she was no longer in the appeals department and trying to contact anyone in that department proved impossible. I was told they could not locate the letter and that I should appeal the denials. When I explained I had already gone through that process and was approved, I was told the procedure was experimental. Obviously, they did not review their own policy manual which showed the procedure was now considered mainstream medicine. Barnes was encountering the same run-around when they tried to pursue bill collection.

This merry-go-round of frustration continued for five months, and I finally contacted the State of Illinois

Department of Insurance and filed an official complaint. All documentation was scanned into my computer and electronically submitted with my complaint. Included was the signed letter approving the stem cell boost from BCBS with the identical codes that they were now denying. I was contacted shortly afterward by my case worker, and she agreed that I had a valid issue and told me to check the status of my complaint regularly on their website. I was genuinely concerned about being on the hook for the $20K+ in medical bills that were not now being approved.

Two days before Christmas, I checked my State of Illinois Department of Insurance account and found that BCBS had just approved my claims for the stem-cell boost. Amazing, how I could not get this approval on my own for five months even with the same documentation, but when the State of Illinois Department of Insurance contacted my medical insurance company, the stem-cell boost was quickly approved!

At my Barnes checkup on December 12 in St. Louis, my oncologist reviewed my white blood counts and saw that in the first half of 2014, I had to give myself 16 Neupogen shots to keep my ANC in acceptable levels. In the second half of 2014, after the stem- cell boost, I only had to use Neupogen four times. He proclaimed the stem-cell boost was a success, and with these better ANC levels, he decided to take me off the Valacyclovir, my final maintenance medication. I had gone from being told I may never be off the maintenance meds to now hearing I was a "free man." 2014 had been an incredibly challenging year, but with the birth of new grandchild, the success of the stem cell boost, the battle won against the insurance company, and getting off the last maintenance medication, I felt renewed going into 2015.

Chapter 11

Immunizations and Challenges (Jan 2015 – Apr 2017)

January 2015 began with exams to check my skin and eyes for any transplant rejection issues, and these exams showed no problems. My ANC stayed within safe ranges after the last shot in December, so I did not have to do any additional Neupogen to start off 2015. My local oncologist had me tested for any resistance to diseases that my new bone marrow could have brought in, and they found some capabilities of my new immune system. However, I still had to repeat all my childhood immunizations which was something I had to do since my old immune system was basically gone.

On January 31, 2015, we had a celebration at the same winery that we had my send off in January 12, 2013 with family and friends. In fact, while I was still in the hospital receiving my transplant, one of the owners of this winery personally delivered Joyce and me several bottles of wine that we were able to enjoy in the weeks following my discharge while still in St. Louis. We enjoyed being back at this winery and all of us celebrated my return. I had moments where deep feelings of gratitude and amazement overcame me, because I would think about what all had happened these last five plus years and especially the last two years. We stressed to everyone that attended that if they were ill, to please not come because of the situation I was still in with a compromised immune system.

However, the last week of January, I was diagnosed with bronchitis and had to take a Z- Pack of antibiotics. This was the first sickness that required a prescription since my transplant but fortunately my new immune system with the help of the prescription responded quickly to this infection, and I was able to kick it in short order. Given the number of stem cell transplant survivors that I saw in St. Louis get upper respiratory infections that caused them major problems, Joyce and I were very anxious about this and were extremely relieved when I recovered by my two-year transplant anniversary. I was now determined to get my immunizations as quickly as possible.

With my ANC counts continuing to be above 1,000, I got a pneumonia vaccine on February 15. That following weekend, I was a guest piano player at another local church, and they asked me to give a short talk at both of their morning services about my ordeal. This was another opportunity for me to share my experiences in my own words in front of a larger group of people, and I was able to give a quick overview of what I had been through these last five plus years. My only focus was to give others hope, and afterward several people came up to me to share their cancer battle stories and how what I shared encouraged them. This was when I began to think about writing this book and focus on communicating to others what Joyce and I had learned through both of our cancer experiences.

The next week, I developed a fever and bad cough, and after visiting my family doctor, I was diagnosed with bronchitis again along with flu-like symptoms. After getting multiple prescriptions to fight this off, my ANC count dropped to 672 on February 25, and I had to give myself another Neupogen shot. Having these two illnesses in the first two months of 2015 created a lot of anxiety about my immune system's ability to keep me healthy. Being in *public* after so much isolation and then getting sick shortly afterwards really made me question my body's ability to ward off illness. The medical team at Barnes was adamant about getting the ANC count above 1,500 which I had not been able to attain since my transplant. My local oncologist was not as concerned about my ANC count being above 1,500. His perspective was that most of these infection fighting cells were "parked" in the lungs and not in the blood stream, so they would be available when needed. They may be available, but my question was whether I had enough of them to keep me from these routine illnesses.

On March 6, I made my last trip down to Barnes Hospital in St. Louis for a checkup. My ANC was 954 and I was not experiencing any of the bone marrow transplant rejection issues that were typically encountered. My nurse practitioner was amazed at my physical condition and activity level at home with my exercise and work schedules. Although she wanted me to come back there for another checkup, I assured her that I would monitor my condition closely utilizing my local family doctor and oncologist. They would be kept informed and I would be back, if necessary. Once again, slowly cutting the cord of overlapping doctor visits helped me emotionally strengthen.

Over the next four months, my ANC counts again dropped into the upper 600's. I gave myself a Neupogen shot in mid-June which kicked my ANC count over 2,200. It stayed up above 1,400 in July without any Neupogen. Joyce and I spent July 18-21 in Cincinnati to visit some friends and watch the Cubs play the Reds. I was a little nervous being in a crowd but was able to go to the ball game and not pick up any illness. At the end of July, I got a TDAP immunization (Tetanus, Diphtheria, and Pertussis). That evening, we attended our granddaughter's summer music group event. Again, I was careful to keep as much distance as possible from people around me to avoid getting anything and used plenty of hand sanitizer. Slowly, Joyce and I learned little *tricks* to avoid the extra germs.

While the handshake is the universal greeting for most, we adapted it to the *elbow bump*. To this day, I do not shake hands because of the risk involved. When we travel, I never put my hands on the railings of stairwells or escalators, and I usually wrap my hand in my outstretched sleeve or the bottom of my jacket to open or shut a door. I now carry with me a small package of sanitizing wipes and use those to wipe down keyboards on computers and pianos that I touch. To the average person, this might seem like overkill, but I have found these small precautions go a long way in keeping me healthy.

Even though my ANC count was 829 in mid-August, my doctor gave me the green light to get the next immunization. It was the MMR shot (Measles, Mumps, Rubella). The first two shots were dead viruses and my doctors were fine with those, but the MMR shot was a live virus which was a major concern that I could get extremely sick from this. My ANC count was 962 on September 15, and I did not get sick from the live virus MMR shot. With the current outbreaks of these diseases, it was vital that I get this immunization to protect myself. I also got my annual flu shot the first part of October, which was the last shot I got for 2015. I did pick up a nasty head cold on October 19, which was the first time getting sick since February. A prescription antibiotic was given as a precaution, and again was able to fight it off without it progressing into a more serious respiratory problem. My ANC count also stayed up above 2,400 in November and 1200 in December with no Neupogen shots.

As my health became better and more stable in 2015, our attentions turned to our elderly mothers who needed more of our help in their living and health situations. My mother had fallen and broken her ankle back in 2010 at age 80. She had lived alone since my father died in 1995 and her health had been fine until the ankle injury. I had encouraged her since that time to get her name on the list to get into the best senior living facility in the Springfield, Illinois area. I knew all about the senior facilities in the area because I had played piano at most of them for over 15 years.

Earlier in 2014, she finally decided to get on the list for the senior living facility that I recommended. We prayed for her to get in and she was approved within a few months. As we were working through this process, her doctors had found a problem with her heart and early in November, she received a pacemaker. In the process, her lung got clipped while the pacemaker was being placed, so she had to go back and get that fixed and the bottom electrode wire reconnected. This fix happened on November 11 and we had to get her moved in the weekend after Thanksgiving 2014. She was not able to get much done to prepare for this move, so my brother and my families all pitched in and got her furniture and other items moved over that weekend. It was a lot of work and with me still recovering from my transplant, I was struggling at times to keep up with everyone. However, it was a huge relief for my mother to be in the senior facility that has every level of care from independent living apartments (where she moved to) all the way up to full nursing home care. It was a big load off my mind to know that she was in a place that could give her the care she needed. She was getting used to her new senior assisted-living apartment and we got her house sold at the beginning of the next year. Even though we live almost an hour from her, I was able to get more involved with her health care appointments and assist her in other areas, which is something I couldn't do while I was battling my own health issues.

My mother-in-law had been in the nursing home since the day before I checked into Barnes Hospital in January 2013 and was needing a lot of attention from Joyce to manage her medications, illnesses, and personal care, such as laundry. She had good nurses taking care of her, but Joyce had to stay engaged and watch closely to ensure her mother's care was up to the level that we wanted. Pauline at age 97 was still cognitively sharp and loved to engage in daily bingo games. Like me, she would battle frequent upper respiratory issues and Joyce usually wore a mask when walking through the halls if there were larger outbreaks of illnesses. This became a challenge for both of us, because if Joyce got sick, my chances of getting the same thing were much higher. Nursing homes frequently had quarantines due to illness outbreaks in the winter months, and the place where Pauline resided was no exception.

With knowledge from our own experiences with medical providers, we both were able to ask key questions to doctors and nurses to help our mothers' get better quality care. Joyce and I worked together to help each other plan and execute the tasks necessary to take care of them while still running our home-based businesses. By mid-summer of that year, Joyce got to take a break from all of this by flying out to LA with our granddaughter to see our son for a week. My immune system was not quite strong enough for airline travel, so I took my mother up to Northern Illinois to visit my daughter and grandson. We both enjoyed our breaks from the busy daily schedules, and it gave us both a respite from the routine we had been on. It was so nice to be able to connect with family that had been so supportive through my journey.

Since I seemed to be physically well, and I was not

experiencing stem cell transplant rejection issues, we also attended the annual Siteman Cancer Center Bone Marrow Transplant Survivor event in downtown St. Louis in mid-September. This annual event had in attendance several hundred people that were survivors and their caretakers. Looking around the room was humbling, as I realized how many others shared similar circumstances to mine and survived. A smaller scale cancer survivor event was held in Decatur in December. I listened closely to other survivors' stories and medical professionals' perspectives on treating patients and their families during these difficult situations. Joyce had already been instrumental in helping people affected by breast cancer in our hometown, and now I began pondering my possible role in becoming more proactive in sharing my story with others.

During these last several years, Joyce had been way overloaded with caring for me and her mother. I tried to do the most that I could to help her, but the long duration of both our health issues began to take its toll on her. She was experiencing more frequent headaches and old car accident neck injuries were really starting to bother her. During the second half of 2015, she started visiting a local pain management practice and getting some injections in her head and neck to relieve some of the pain. Then while putting up Christmas decorations after Thanksgiving, she fell off a small step ladder and broke two ribs. We called our family doctor and he told her that going to the emergency room would not provide any help. She would just have to stop her activities and rest. Fortunately, I was in good enough health to help her now. Sleeping in a recliner while the ribs healed was beneficial for her neck pain. Once she was able to lie flat again, we made the switch to an adjustable bed frame which kept her from needing any more pain injections. Funny how things that seem bad at the time can lead to positive changes down the road.

Since I had been able to be in crowd situations several times and not get sick, we decided to fly for a short getaway to Fort Myers, Florida, from January 10 – 14, 2016. The fresh seafood was great for every lunch and dinner, and I was able to fly there and back without any health issues. Those short walks on the beach refreshed my mind and body. This was just the latest in many small steps to try and get me back to a more normal lifestyle in 2016. I thought I was finally past having to be so anxious about my immune system coming up on my third transplant anniversary. Well, I was wrong.

At the beginning of February, I noticed a small rash on my left forehead and had what I thought was a bad sinus headache. With recent significant weather changes, I figured I was just dealing with my typical sinus problems. However, after a couple of days, I started experiencing sharp pains shooting down the left side of my face. Joyce thought I might have shingles and sent pictures to our family doctor who confirmed the diagnosis. I immediately got an oral anti-viral prescription started that evening (hello Valacyclovir again), but since it takes a while for the prescription to start working the rash spread around my left eye a few days later. This was extremely dangerous to my sight and while still dealing with the shooting pain, my family doctor sent me to an eye doctor to monitor my condition.

Having shingles after an allogeneic stem cell transplant was not unusual since my immune system had been compromised for a while and the anti-viral drugs kept this at bay in the early stages of my recovery. However, unlike most stem cell transplant survivors, I did not experience any significant issues like this for these last three years.

We posted this issue on my Caring Bridge site to let everyone know about this latest issue and again asked for prayer. I believe that communicating my needs to people over this website and their prayers for healing were a key reason why I had not experienced any significant rejection issues and my recovery had progressed as well as it had to this point. After 15 days, the shingles rash began subsiding, and the pain had stopped but now intense itching occurred as the rash areas on my face and head began to heal. A prescription skin cream and Aloe Vera gel helped some, but I was miserable from this itching and could not get any significant relief nor much sleep for weeks. This again affected my emotional state and caused me to struggle with dark thoughts and negative moods. While I knew the cancer was gone, I wondered what physical issues and their consequences awaited. As someone who had gone nearly fifty years of life with few infirmities, I was again struck with the reality that these fragile bodies can be struck down at any moment. Even in my darkest days, and there were many, I clung to my hope in Christ and the reality that all these struggles were temporary.

By the middle of March 2016, my ANC blood count was 1294 and the next blood check was scheduled for May. Going two months between blood tests seemed like an eternity given how often I had been getting my blood checked. The shingles rash and itching were gone but I still had some tingling in those areas where the rash was. My doctors confirmed that this tingling feeling is due to the nerve damage done by having shingles; but I did not sustain any eye damage or any other significant long-term issues. Again, I attribute my recovery from the shingles to my prayer support and God's mercy.

Even through this latest challenge, I was able to continue working, playing piano and exercising. I found this is another key to dealing with a major health crisis, when possible get back to your normal routines and be as active as possible. In middle of May, we went to Milwaukee to see a couple of Cubs-Brewers games. By staying at the same hotel as the Cubs players, Joyce and I got to personally meet several players, coaches, and media people. Since this was the second MLB outing since the transplant, I felt more at ease than I did when we were in Cincinnati the previous summer. Ever diligent, we took all the needed precautions while being in the crowds.

At the end of June, we got our granddaughter for a week and attended my nephew's wedding. Life was finally starting to have some semblance of normalcy. My full physical exam and tests were completed on July 7, 2016. Everything checked out fine and my ANC blood count was

1130. Still not over the 1500 level, but with my recovery from the shingles, apparently it was high enough to do the job. We walked the survivor lap at our local Relay for Life event that month and talked with many other survivors and medical people. Throughout both our cancer battles, we have gotten to know many people involved in the struggles against various forms of this disease. Joyce took another trip to LA with our granddaughter at the end of July into the beginning of August to get a break while I was able to handle everything on the home front. As much as I would have liked to have gone, we felt it was necessary for one of us to be here to attend to the needs of our moms.

I made the decision when I came back from St. Louis to take back less computer work and help with the garment business more. I tired more easily than I used to and driving up and down the roads in Central Illinois exacerbated that. I was also concerned about being in more public places and working on customer's infected computers. I certainly did not want the unseen bacteria to infect me. When Joyce returned, we installed new equipment to increase our garment heat-press capacity at our home office. Our garment and computer businesses continued to keep us both busy which was absolutely needed to keep ahead of the bills. Working mostly from home gave me an added sense of security where my health was concerned.

Given the shingles outbreak, I did not get any immunizations during 2016 except a flu shot on October 27. My annual checkup with my local oncologist on December 13 went great with my ANC blood count holding steady at

1130. I was doing well until just before Christmas when I got a stomach flu with a fever. I had to stay home and miss family Christmas events over the weekend which hit me awfully hard emotionally. I had been looking forward to seeing family at several gatherings but could not attend. I sunk down into a depression that I had not experienced since being in the hospital with the transplant. The isolation and feeling sick took me back to those dark times when my future was very uncertain. Watching Joyce walk out of the house with all the packages for the rest of the family was so emotionally painful that I just sat on the couch and stared out the window most of the afternoon while she was gone. In my mind I knew this was a brief blip on the radar and that I would not be in confinement long, but the PTSD aspects of this journey took me back to the darkness of isolation I was trying so much to avoid.

Emotional swings I found are very unpredictable and can hit quickly and with great severity. I decided to go see my family doctor on January 6, 2017, to discuss this situation with him and get his input. I could not put my finger on it, but something was just not right. He had me get a blood draw to determine my thyroid, testosterone, and Vitamin D levels. The first two were within normal ranges, however, the vitamin D level was at the exceptionally low end of the normal range and could be a significant contributing factor. To remedy this, he told me to get on 5,000 units of vitamin D daily and continue my healthy diet and regular exercise. He also shared that he regularly sees people in my age group (55 and above) that deal with the *doldrums*. I understand that at 56 years old I can experience that, and I had several close friends around my age and older who struggled with mild depression. With children now grown and out on their own and physically not having the energy every day that used to be, mild depression and feeling down (*doldrums* as my doctor explained it) were quite common. Couple that with not being as driven with career and financial goals and it was understandable how all the ingredients were there to experience depressive days.

However, ever since the allogeneic stem cell transplant in 2013, I noticed my moods were much more volatile and subject to change than before. I had always been very stable emotionally, but now I noticed that at any time I could begin crying or feeling upset without understanding exactly why. I had lunch with a friend whose wife also had a low Vitamin D level and experienced similar mild depression and lack of energy that I was struggling with. He was adamant that I needed to get my Vitamin D level up. After a couple of weeks on the Vitamin D supplement, I did feel less depressed and had more energy. My wife also had me take a St. John's Wort daily herbal supplement to help deal with the negative moods that were seeming to occur more frequently at this time. While I knew my doctor would give me an antidepressant if I requested it, I was not at the level of needing something that strong. Had these things not worked, I certainly would have gotten that prescription medication.

As 2017 continued I realized that I now have two birthdays each year to celebrate. Larry V2.0 was four years old on 02/06/17, and Larry V1.0 was 57 years old on

04/22/17! During this time, I took some time to reflect on my experiences on being a cancer survivor and especially going through the allogeneic stem cell transplant process and recovery. I found that I had much more appreciation for every day that I was well physically, emotionally, and mentally. For most of my life, I was focused on future goals like education degrees, career, wealth, having and raising a family. Since I never had any significant health issues, I assumed my physical body would always be well and be able to function the ways I wanted it to. Boy, did I find out that is not necessarily a guarantee! I didn't think I was taking my health for granted, and I certainly saw what Joyce went through in her forties with her cancer battle and the subsequent early menopause, but the reality was I really didn't think all this would happen to me. That false sense of security was quickly broken down when I got my own life-changing diagnosis. The real *reality* is that each of us is only one phone call or doctor visit away from life altering disease or disability.

I also wanted to help people around me as well as live out the Christian concepts laid out in God's Word as I went through this ordeal. Jesus Christ taught many things about how we are to live on this earth to honor Him, and after becoming a Christian in 1984, that had always been and continues to be my top priority. My internal perspective continued changing through this time to focus much more on being grateful for the daily gifts that I previously took for granted. This also helped my moods be better overall because I was listening more for the Holy Spirit's direction and seeking His perspective as my life unfolded.

I now understand that life changes can and do occur unexpectedly and quickly, and that everyone's human existence is a series of different temporary seasons. While my season of illness was unforeseen through my lens, I know there will be new hurdles to face with both my immune system and any other challenges that may come against me.

As Moses requested God in Psalm 90, "teach us to number our days that we may gain a heart of wisdom." I found out that we can and should do the right things for our bodies' physical, mental, and emotional health. Just as important are the spiritual growth exercises for our eternal existence through biblical teachings and indwelling by the Holy Spirit. Without that there is no truly fulfilling, satisfying, sustainable, victorious living with peace and contentment. Life on this earth is very temporary, and all material things and relationships do change and eventually end, but the relationship with my Creator never ends.

Coming face to face with a life-threatening illness forces you to grasp your mortality, and as I age and the things of this world lose their attraction to me, my future goals and focus are to become as prepared as possible for my eternal life. I am constantly reminded that the temporary physical body I am walking around in right now will one day be replaced with an eternal one. The sting of death, which we all will face one day, is momentary compared to the glorious existence living forever in an eternal body that will never grow old, get sick or have any of the problems we face down here. I truly can say I walked through the valley of the shadow of death, but by His mercy, I am still here to proclaim all He has done. Some earthly journeys are much longer and more difficult than mine, but no journey needs to be tackled alone. Tap into and apply the resources of God's Word, prayer, the outpouring of the Holy Spirit and people who really want to help. Bless you on your life's journey, and always remember to look up…

Larry Mazzotti

APPENDIX 1

A t one of the annual survivor events, my wife, who as a recent breast cancer survivor had started a local HER Breast Cancer Support Group (Helping Each Other Recover) and participated in many other very public activities to educate, train and support local cancer support groups, was the featured speaker. Here is what she shared about her "survival kit" that she used to get through her cancer battle.

Do you remember, as a child, having a survival kit? It was small plastic box that contained a water bottle, a candy bar, a flashlight, maybe —all the things "needed" to survive while you and your friends played an imaginary game of being stranded in the woods or on a deserted island. As cancer survivors, we have a different type of survival kit, and we'll carry it with us for the duration of our lives. So I ask you today, what's in your survival kit?? Each kit has different things that have helped us in living with, through, and beyond that cancer diagnosis. I'd like to tell you about my kit today. In it, I carry with me knowledge, endurance, faith, hope, and compassion. I am a breast cancer survivor. And although a part of me is gone, cancer did not take away the person inside me. Whatever *you* have faced in your personal cancer journey, realize that today we are here to celebrate our status as survivors.

Hearing the word "survivor" always brought to mind images on the evening news of plane crashes or ships sinking. Survivor in that context is someone who has come through a terrible ordeal and persevered to the other side— victorious. A cancer survivor has done the same. Most of us here today have gone through that ordeal of diagnosis and treatment or you are one of the medical professionals or family or friends of a very special person who today claims victory in the title "survivor".

Knowledge is the first thing that arrived in my "kit". Empowering ourselves with information makes the choices easier. From the time I found the lump just before Christmas, 1997, through my surgeries and chemotherapy, and to this day, I arm myself with accurate information through reliable sources about the latest in breast cancer prevention, screening, and treatment. For as we can testify here today, one of the keys to surviving cancer is early detection. My initial biopsy confirmed it was cancer. Both my surgeon and my oncologist recommended a lumpectomy, which is removal of the lump, a small area of marginal tissue around the lump, and a sampling of lymph nodes. This would be followed by 3 months of chemo and then radiation. I was told this could be done successfully only if there was no cancer in the lymph glands or the margins. My surgeon called one week later: "Joyce, there's good news and bad news—the lymph glands were clear, but the margins were not—we have to go back in and take the breast." Without accurate information at this vital stage, this entire process would've been much more frightening.

Knowledge of the situation came through again when I was told that the hair goes two weeks after the first treatment. And somewhere in the midst of surgeries and treatment, endurance was added to my survival kit, because knowledge alone was not enough to get me through what I was about to face.

One evening I gently pulled at the back of my hair, and a clump about an inch wide came out easily in my hand. The next day I gave my husband the clippers and told him to take it all off. My kids were a little shocked at first, but G.I. Jane was the popular movie at that time. If Demi Moore can do it—I could, too. I became "G.I. Mom". I certainly didn't get the compensation Demi did, but I learned that endurance does build character.

Like most of you, I really came to depend on my wig. Don't ask me why, but they name wigs after women's names. It was called "Sammi", and she was like a faithful pet. But Sammi let me down once. On a very windy day in April, I was walking out of the Junior High in Mt. Zion. Somehow the wind got under that long canopy and boom, the wig was gone and was tumbling behind me on the sidewalk as fast as I was chasing it. It also happened that the Junior High show choir was getting their group picture taken less than 30 feet from where I was. I held my breath and waited for the gasps or the laughter. There was neither. It was so cold that day, and those poor girls were shivering so much, they didn't even notice me. I grabbed the wig, slapped it on my head, and ran to the van. I looked up in the mirror and saw I had put it on sideways. I started crying and then laughing—humor goes a long way to building endurance. Thank goodness the wig stayed on the sidewalk and not into the many puddles that were all around.

There were good days and bad ones. Sometimes the sores in my mouth were so bad I couldn't eat. Many days the food just tasted like aluminum foil. When I felt like working, I did. With a home-based business, my hours were flexible. I learned everything is not an A-priority, and sometimes it's good to just rest and reflect. But mostly, I learned it was not my strength alone, or the knowledge alone, or the endurance I was building daily that was getting me through this battle. It was my faith in Jesus Christ. There were days when I needed peace so badly, and he gave me peace. There were days when I mourned the loss of my hair and my breast, and he gave me gladness in the fact that I was alive and that each of these experiences could help me help someone else going through breast cancer. Faith for me, was, and still is the single most important item in my survival kit.

Faith in my doctors and the many medical professionals who were doing the busy work of my treatment was also crucial. I had faith then, as now, that God was guiding them through the decision-making methods and making the appropriate recommendations. God and the medical staff were partners in the process of my healing. He was directing their steps, as the prayers of so many friends and loved ones were getting me through this cancer journey no one is ever ready to take. I had to learn to walk by faith, not by sight, because I knew outwardly I neither looked nor felt well. I had to walk in faith, not in fear, which was by far my biggest personal obstacle. Facing my fears, although difficult at times to do, has given me peace.

Along with faith, comes hope. Hope for a cure, hope that the cancer never returns, hope for many more tomorrows. Hope also tells me that life here is real, but temporary. Hope is there because the One who is in all will see us through it all. My hope is in God who knows what I need, regardless of what I wish for. Part of the terror of a potentially fatal disease lies in the feelings of isolation, that sense that the path in front of you has disappeared. Because of hope, God shed light on these fears and reflected back a pathway lit, not blocked, by my sense of mortality. Hope is a gift, given to us, to be given to others in their time of need. Hope is the promise of restoration—and while cancer can initially shatter our dreams, hope can revive and renew what we thought was lost.

Another gift born by suffering is the gift of compassion and giving comfort. Compassion is a powerful component of the survival kit, because whether we choose to be bitter or to be a blessing is our choice alone. **We** have to make that choice. If we choose to be victims rather than to make the most of our difficulties, we miss out on the very things that can empower us.

Having been through the personal pain of cancer has helped me to recognize and respond to the pain in the lives of others. When our pain carries us beyond ourselves and into the hearts and lives of other hurting people, it has accomplished its best work—it has taught us to love. There are so many areas of need in breast cancer patients. From knowing what questions to ask the doctors to "where can I find a wig?", to "I'm afraid", there is such an opportunity to reach out to other women once they received that diagnosis. Through a network of local survivors and healthcare workers, *Helping Each Other Recover* was begun. This group is a one-on-one information and support network for women who are newly diagnosed with breast cancer. By expressing love and concern in the worst possible situations, these HER volunteers are encouraged, the personal pain is minimized, and satisfaction is obtained in knowing others can benefit from what we've gone through. Since the program was begun nearly a year ago, women are finding that having a friend to talk to can help them get through the initial trauma of breast cancer.

The wonderful thing about compassion, is that it is not just confined to the person being treated for cancer. Where would we be without the compassion of the doctors, and the dear nurses who daily must calm the fears of cancer patients as they draw blood, administer chemo, and assist in the clinical trials which will eventually benefit all of us? On behalf of all of us here today, I just want to thank you all for the stressful jobs you endure for us! And then there's the people who prayed, brought in meals, and assisted in ways too numerous to count while I was going through surgery and treatment. And of course, my wonderful husband and my family and friends, who were with me each day of this journey. How could I ever express my thanks for the compassion they showed me at times when I didn't look or feel very lovable. Is there someone special who helped you?

I was on the other side of this experience at one time, too. My first experience with cancer was watching my mother go through her mastectomy almost 12 years ago. With determination, she painfully submitted to those annual check-ups and tests. I watched as she tried to rebuild the strength in her arm, and as she guarded it carefully against injury and infection. We both claim victory here today, as do all of you who have waged this war against cancer.

Unfortunately, sometimes things are more bittersweet. I wish my father was here today, but we lost him in November after he waged a one-month battle with leukemia. At age 94, he knew the odds were not in his favor, but because of his faith in Jesus Christ, he faced the end with courage and grace in the ultimate healing.

So I ask you again, what is in your survival kit? Do you have the things mentioned? Perhaps yours is larger or smaller, because cancer survival is a very individual thing. I've gathered some other things along the way, and I'm sure you have, too. Can we see a cure in our lifetime? Sure we can. It can happen! This day, and every day I have here is precious to me. Thank God for every day *you* have and use it to the fullest.

Made in the USA
Monee, IL
09 October 2020